Diary

of a

Vicarage

Cat

Rev'd Christine French

with love
Christine

British Library Cataloguing in Publication Data.
A catalogue record for this book is available from the British Library

ISBN 978 0 86071 767 6

A Commissioned Publication Printed by

MOORLEYS
Print, Design & Publishing
info@moorleys.co.uk · www.moorleys.co.uk

Narrative of Florence's Diary

Introduction to Florence

Florence is a special cat. All cats are special in their own unique and individual way. A little white kitten was found abandoned walking around Nottingham, lost and on her own, so she was taken to Millwood Cat Rescue. They soon realised she was deaf. At the Rescue Centre she had the 'Queen's Operation' and then a new home had to be found. It soon became apparent how feisty and independent this disabled cat was. A volunteer at the Centre mentioned to Rev Christine about this cat needing a home where it was safe to go out, keeping this young cat in made her stressful.

So it was, Rev Christine took her husband, popped in on the Centre, under the guise of supporting their Open Day, for him to meet this special cat. Hesitantly he agreed for her to come home with them but they hadn't got a cat carrier with them so it would have to wait. Rev Christine immediately got a cat carrier from the car boot and the rest was history.

Originally called 'Katie' the volunteer suggested a new name and so the little feisty deaf cat was re-named 'Florence' and moved into the Vicarage at Bunny village near Nottingham.

Her guardians soon realised they had got their hands full with her as she climbed to the tops of trees higher than the house, and became a regular visitor at church and the neighbours' houses. Everyone soon knew Florence! And so her adventures began.

Great joy was proclaimed in the French household when Florence was voted 'Ilkeston Advertiser – Pet of the Year 2015'. Frustratingly, due to a mix up and mis-communication between the pet shop running the competition and the newspaper, the prize was given to a dog, but Florence was pleased to know that she rightfully had the most votes and the title. Fame was to follow Florence in 2014 when in September she appeared on the front of the Newark Advertiser with an interview on Page 5 as she invited everyone to a 'Pet Praise' service at Norwell Church.

Once again shouts of jubilation were heard at the Kirk Hallam Vicarage when in January 2018 the Nottingham Post declared Florence was 'Nottingham Post Pet of the Year 2017'. She took all this in her stride, not letting this on-going fame change the little cat she is. Later in 2018 the Cat's Protection League nominated Florence to be 'Cat of the Year' in the category of 'Outstanding Rescue Cat', where she made it into the final three.

Glossary of Florence's Language and Terminology

Business   This generally means poo.

Cat-top   Laptop.

Changing Picture Box Television, may also be called a 'Moving Picture Box'.

Days   Monday - Moan-day – because people moan about it.

Tuesday – Choose-day – because people choose to do the same again.

Wednesday – Wet-knees-day – because this is the evening she spends sitting in the indoor puddle, with her knees being wet.

Thursday – Furrs-day.

Friday – Fry-day because it's the day he has fried fish for tea.

Saturday – Cat-a-day – the day they should stay at home and honour their cats.

Sunday – Fun-day, when Florence has fun at church.

Happy Snappy Game Involves Florence jumping or swiping at unsuspecting others – cats and humans as they pass by.

Hissy steamy thing   The iron.

Holiday Prison   The cattery.

Indoor puddles   The bath.

Indoor rain   The shower.

Metal Wheelie Boxes	Cars.
Spinny thing	The washing machine.
Tail flick	It's a bit like giving the 'V's with your fingers.
Wiggly finger	It's being told off.

Week 1 - Cats & Kittens

Sometimes it's rather hard living with cats. Not for my guardians living with me, obviously, but sometimes it's rather hard for me to be living with all these other cats my guardians insist on giving a loving home to. Let me explain in more detail. Missy likes to think she is the powerful Matriarch of our pack, why? Because she, accompanied by her son 'Nervous Nipper' have been here the longest. However she does annoy me, and hisses and spits at me and the other cats without any reason, I call her 'Hissy Missy' because she is so grumpy. Nipper used to be fun when he was younger, and we used to play together a lot, but as I grew up and got stronger he stopped playing with me, saying I was 'too rough' – he really is a big mummy's boy.

Padgely is lots more fun, I do my sideways arch back walk and he turns his head and we then jump up at each other, and chase each other around the garden, until we run out of breath. He's such fun, and so gentle, when he does catch me it's only play fighting, and never minds if I hit him rather hard. He's like the perfect gentle big brother.

Then there is Jasper who looks like Padgely except grumpier and a lot older. I'm not sure how old Jasper is but he's seen more winters than I've got claws. Jasper just wants to inspect everybody's meals and eat every food he can find. Jasper is the boss, but I'm not frightened of him, we used to hate each other as he was a bit of a bully but I stood up to him and now we respect each other.

Pippin – Pips moved in when we moved here, I think she came with the Vicarage, like the carpets and curtains. I really hated her to start with, she was friendly, perky and happy, everyone loved her, and my guardians kept feeding her and fussing her. On reflection Pips has taught me a lot, she's taught me to learn to love the stranger, to realise we need to help our neighbours, and those in need. Strangely she loves going to church, and by following her I too now am a regular at church, she goes to everything she can, and so brave around people, I'm not as brave as her but I'm getting better and certainly not as nervous as Nipper.

Week 2 - Dogs & Doggy Doings

I love watching the world go by as I sit outside the front of the Vicarage. This is an ideal opportunity to observe humans going about their lives and routines but also it gives me an insight into the 'world of dogs'. I'm not keen on some dogs, but I am happy with others. What does amaze me is how some humans need to be led by their dogs I presume, otherwise the humans would get lost and never go home again. I see it morning after morning, the same humans holding tightly to their dogs lead as the dog is pulling them on to walk forward and walk quicker. Maybe these are lazy humans who need the exercise, but they all look fit and healthy to me. I'm just not sure what it is all about.

I remember last year how the old chap that came daily to church had a little Jack Russell, on the disc on her collar it said 'Freda' so I'm guessing that's her name. On this day Freda wasn't on her lead and when she saw me sat outside the Vicarage, she started to run at me. I jumped through the cat shaped hole in the garden gate, only to have Freda following me and closing in on me. It was as we ran across the lawn to the bushes on the far side that Freda did actually catch up with me, I think I must have lost my footing and slipped a little. As I slipped, I cunningly turned my agile body around to see the look of shock in her eyes and without a second thought hit her on the nose, she then turned around and started to run out of the garden, with me chasing her! Such fun. But as I was about to leap after her through the

3

hole in the black gate my guardian came rushing out of the back door looking confused and stopped this excellent game of chase by firmly picking me up and holding on to me. How my heart was pounding from all that fast running.

Not all dogs are fun to play with, take for instance the dog where my friends George and Darwin live on the neighbouring close. I used to go over there regularly and sit on their wheelie bins, looking into their front room, and their dog would jump up at the inside of the window, opening and closing its mouth, sometimes quite quickly and often with a snarled lip as well. Okay I admit it, I wasn't always very nice to their old cat Kitty, I've learnt not to chase her. I think I was a bit jealous of how cute she was. But now we have learnt to forgive each other and things are a lot more fun, as George and Darwin regularly come over to play in my garden again.

Week 3 - Smell & Smelling Things

I love smelling things. I can learn a lot from a deep breath in and a slow breath out. I can easily pick up from the air if a cat has recently been there and which cat it was. If a dog has been around. But the best smells are food smells. Sometimes the food in my bowl just doesn't smell right so I walk off and leave it after just one quick lick. I can see this really annoys my guardians, but they just don't understand. Smell is important to me and if it doesn't smell right then it won't taste right either.

When my guardian is cooking a chicken in the oven, the aroma of the roasting chicken fills the whole house, I begin to drool without realising it. And poor Beasley kitten goes half mad with the irresistible smell, forcing him to spend ages in the kitchen waiting for our guardian to open the oven door and get the fat bird out to carve up. Yes my guardian has it for his lunch but he's very kind and always shares some with us moggies.

Outside is full of smells. Not just the fragrance of flowers, bushes and trees when flowering, but lots of other rich smells too. The pond stinks, the stench of fish is rather unique to me but Jasper loves the pond and daily laps up some of the fishy tasting and fishy smelling water. His breath stinks too.

The hens smell, well to be precise their hen house smells. Sometimes, when it's just had its weekly clean it smells lovely, of fresh straw and sawdust and of dried grass – such a tempting smell, beckoning me to come in and have a snooze, but I don't, the hens are bullies and would happily peck me if they found me in their house. But a day or two before it gets cleaned out it pongs, of hen poo. Why do they do their 'business' inside their own home, what dirty filthy animals hens are, they should be more like us cats and cover over any 'business' as soon as it's done.

Then there is the smell in the air on a warm summer's evening, it drifts over houses, garages, and gardens and into my nostrils, wow, the smell of meat being cooked in the open air, often the savoury fragrance wafts in from different directions, so I guess just as all ants know when it's right to grow wings and fly, all humans have an instinct to know when it's the right time to cook outside.

Week 4 - Water Wonders

Now as much as the next cat, I love a drink. Sometimes my tipple is a cool refreshing gulp of water, and I've got my guardians trained to leave several water bowls around my home, but then just as the water begins to have a lovely stale taste, she goes and washes the bowls and changes the water. She seems to do it every other day. But when she's not here and he is left in charge, the water may not be changed for several days, getting more stale, sometimes with a dead fly floating in it – delicious.

And then there are the drinking fountains. The one upstairs has water coming out of a little hole and I try to catch the water in my mouth before it hits the bowl – its great fun, sometimes more water ends up on the carpet than in my mouth – she gives me one of 'those looks' as she watches me play but I know she really thinks it's funny. The one downstairs has water running down a slide into a deep bowl, rather than catching the water in my mouth I try to dam it with my paw, letting the water build up until it runs over the side and down into the rug. Again, if she sees me playing I get one of 'those stares' and a wag of her finger at me. I've come to realise that her wagging her figure is not good news, like when a dog wags its tail, but rather the opposite, it means I'm going to get shoo-ed away and ignored.

I love the fishy tasting water in the pond outside. In Winter it is warmer than you'd expect and in summer it is still cool and refreshing. I've never caught a fish when drinking, but I have seen them come nearby, investigating what is causing the little ripples in the murky pond water. Of course, there is the added bonus that I might get to catch a frog. Several of them live in and near the pond and they are great fun as they jump around when I chase them. I've never caught one yet,  but once when playing chase he came out and caught the frog in his big hands, which is cheating, and I guess he knew this, as he put the frog back into the pond.

Then the best drink – well its water again, but from a glass by her bedside, it has to be the best water, because when I go to have a lick or two she moves it away from me! Little does she know sometimes I do get to have a sip or two without her seeing!

Week 5 - Playing Games & Getting Older

Over time, things change and we change. I remember 6 years ago when I was a kitten, I did play a lot more then. Toys which excited me - like ping pong balls bouncing all over the hall on the shiny laminate floor and onto the hard walls and back again, well now they are just a bit dull. When younger I used to chase the feathery thing which my guardian would make go one way and then another, faster and faster until I got dizzy and had to sit down in a heap before falling down. I think he thought it was like a little bird, I knew it was just a couple of feathers on a bit of old string but I would still chase and pounce on it to keep him happy. My absolute favourite game, which I was easily the best at, far better than any of the other cats, was climbing trees. Gosh I could run up the trunks so fast and climb from a thick branch to a thinner one, and so on, higher and higher. Indeed I remember one time climbing so high I could see straight in to the bedroom window – that gave them a shock when they looked out from the first floor bedroom to see me staring straight back at them. They didn't look pleased to see me, but apparently they wanted to join in the fun, as she seemed to dance around the base of the tree, he hurriedly started to climb the tree to join me, but using a long step ladder – I think that's called cheating. Why do we grow out of things? Why do we stop doing the simple things in life that bring us so much fun? She now puts on a DVD for me to watch – with lots of birds, mice and fish and leaves me to it. I'd rather she picked up that bit of old string with the chewed up feathers on it and we played again together.

Well this Springtime I'm going to recapture my inner kitten and embrace things I thought I'd grown out of; playing 'Hide and Seek' in the bushes with Pips; pretend kung-fu fighting with Padgely; and drinking from the fish pond to try to catch a fish. I hope the other cats can recapture their inner kitten too.

Week 6 – Sleeping & Snoozing

Although in February (or 'Furrbury' as I think it's really called) and the days are getting a little longer, and the first sign of Spring can be seen in the little snow drops poking through the hard soil, it is still rather cold. When out and about around the churchyard my little feet do get chilly, then go numb and start to tingle. While the weather is cold George, my friend, doesn't come out to play anymore, but Darwin his younger brother is braver, and we spend more time together, sitting at the bottom of the big tree and watching the squirrels run and jump through its branches, they are amazing and so fast. I do like my new special friend. After a while when even my ears are tingling I retreat into the home. I can understand why my humans seem to prefer (or should that be 'purr-furr') staying in by a warm fire.

Now us cats are experts at many things, especially sleeping. We cats can sleep for over 20 hours each day, and the two elderly cats that live at the Vicarage do that every day, in fact they seem to do very little of anything else. I think they are just very lazy, as they can move and run away quickly when they see me sneaking into play chase with them. Why do my humans make such a strange fuss about sleeping? Us cats will look for somewhere comfortable to nap, or something snuggly to sleep on, or even better, someone warm to curl up on. And that's it, off to the land of nod. My human creatures have got the first part okay, they settle down on the sofas, watching the moving picture window (I do love the nature shows, and really enjoyed sitting right in front of it to watch the 'Blue Planet II' programmes and batting the fish with my left paw – it's such fun, but my humans obviously don't agree as they keep moving me away from the screen). Then they often fall asleep but then just after a short time of snoozing, they wake up, and rather than  curling back up and drifting off again, then they start rushing around, brushing their teeth, changing into special clothes for sleeping and going upstairs into the big bed. It seems ridiculous because after all that fuss and running around, now they are wide awake and it takes several more hours before they are back in the land of nod again. Really humans, watch cats and learn from us!

Week 7 - Sunday or Fun-day Services

Now 'Fun-day' is the day which I love for several reasons. My guardian puts on her long white clothes (obviously copying my fur) and goes into the church after she's had her breakfast – and of course fed me and the other cats before that. He is still lying in the bed – ready to be pounced on and feet attacked if I get a bit bored. But I don't, not on Fun-days, as I follow my guardian over to the old church and observe them from the doorway. After they have all gathered together, several things seem to happen. They all look at her and sit down, she moves her lips for a short while and then they all stand up, this repeats several times, including at one point, she or another dressed in long robes walks to the middle of the church carrying the big red book that normally lives on the Altar. After a minute or two they walk back and everyone sits down, while my guardian goes up the stone steps to the wooden box that sticks out from the wall. On several occasions I've joined her in the box, she doesn't look best pleased to see me, and I don't help myself by trying to get my balance on the wooden stand and knocking her bits of paper everywhere.

Shortly after she comes down from the wooden box, they all stand up and hold each other's hand, I don't think they are playing a game of 'Ring A Ring A Roses' but it does have some similarities although no one sneezes, and no one falls down. After this then she walks up and stands behind the Altar, waving her arms about while there are wafers and wine on that table, and then she shares it with everyone. So, I got myself into a good viewing position on a little table next to the rail where they kneel or stand to receive it. Gosh it was rather moving to observe them all coming forward, with such emotions on their face, they didn't notice me as they were thinking, I guess they were thinking about what it meant to share the bread and wine with each other. It looked like it was very symbolic for them as there were so many emotions expressed in their faces. Then shortly after that the service ended with more standing up and sitting down. I'm not exactly sure what happens but it seems to matter to them. And then I come out from my observation point and get lots of fuss again, as does Pips too as she's normally hanging around. The more I observe my humans, the less I understand and the more there is to keep observing.

Week 8 - Birds, My Feathery Friends

Birds are cheats. Cats can run, jump and climb but we cannot fly. Birds fly and that's just cheating. Take for instance last week, I was out in the garden, with my special friend Darwin and we sat under a bush together at the bottom of the tree waiting. We waited for ages, not moving, just watching and waiting, which wasn't easy as the dampness in the air turned to fine drizzle and then that turned into light rain. Darwin and I had to snuggle together to keep dry under the waxy leaves. Every morning my guardian puts out a mixture of seeds and nuts which the birds and squirrels love to scoff up. Sometimes the garden seems full of birds, but as I approach them, they all seem to know I'm coming and all flutter their wings and fly off. The hens were more fun, they didn't fly away, I could play chase with them. The little cockerel would flap his wings and run round the lawn with me in hot pursuit of him, it was such fun – with both of us soon becoming out of breath and me slowing down and coming to a halt as he headed into the hen house. Such fun.

So back to the 'Pigeon Ambush' or more correctly 'Pigeon By a Bush', I wait nearby to bounce out on them and play chase. And that's just what Darwin and I were doing last week. The fat pigeons couldn't really see us, hiding behind the green waxy leaves, so flew down and started to happily peck away at the free nosh, even though the rain was coming down more heavily, it didn't stop them from their free breakfast. So greedy were they that both Darwin and I simultaneously stepped forward, but as a tiny little twig broke under my paw, the pigeons looked directly at me, and then as I leapt forward towards the fat feathery thing, it flapped its wings and flew up, up and away in a second.

Well Darwin wasn't happy and nor was I. What had happened to let that fat chap of a pigeon know I was there. Sometimes I do feel like I'm missing something that the other cats have. Being deaf sometimes makes life an uphill struggle. But next time I'll know not to step on any twigs and one time I will 'tag' a pigeon and win that game.

Week 9 - Food & Treats

I'm not a picky cat, but I know what I like and I like what I know. And that's never truer than with my food. Most cat food is gross. I don't know how the other cats eat it, it's sloppy, and messy and smells dreadful. I like my dry biscuits, they are fun to eat, I enjoy crunching them in my teeth, and the taste fills my mouth, and the smell fills my nostrils, I do enjoy my biscuits. But I'll try other food, recently I've really enjoyed the little tins of paté cat food. It is whipped up into a light mousse and melts on my tongue as I enjoy licking it out of my bowl, this is often a supper time treat in the front room. But my favourite has to be when she opens a tin of tuna and divides it between a few of us cats, the smell of tuna fills the house and where ever I am I come running for this special treat.

Something I also enjoy is the occasional treat of a cold, sweet cream that she squirts into my bowl – I'm not sure what exactly this squirty treat is but I do love it, especially on a hot day.

But of course, the best food is somebody else's food. Now her food rarely excites me, it's all green, leafy and bland, occasionally there is a tasty bit of cheese for the taking but not often. However his food is a different matter. While he is switching on the TV I've sneaked over to his plate and sneaked off with mouthful of tuna – spitting out any sweetcorn bits – who likes sweet corn? Also I've swiped a slice of tasty beef when he's got his back turned. But it's Jasper who is the most blatant, Jasper will sit on the arm of the sofa, right next to him, and as he puts his fork up to his mouth Jasper will strike out his paw, hitting the food and knocking it off. He'll keep doing this while the man laughs and then he stops laughing and moves Jasper out of the room, it's like Jasper is a Food Inspector and has to examine what he's eating!

Week 10 - Funerals & the Big Box

Being the Vicar's cat means I do get to observe some strange human behaviours, none more so than the big box routine. I'm not sure what it is about the big box, but generally every week one is brought into the church. Most times there are lots of people waiting for the big box to arrive, some go into church before it arrives, and some wait outside until it pulls up in a big smart car. The people are all very sad, many are tearful, and it's not hayfever either, with all the beautiful flowers that are arranged in stunning tributes on the big box. Several people solemnly carry the big box into the church, but I don't think they are very good with directions as my guardian has to lead them in every time and then the tearful people follow them. Now I don't go into church on these occasions, but Pips does, and on one such occasion she jumped onto the big box – oh my guardian was furious with her for days, I don't think any of the sad people were, they fussed her and smiled at her, they looked kind people.

Now my favourite bit is when the men who carried the big box into church come out, having left the box in there with everyone. I get lots of fuss from them while strolling around their legs and leaving a trail of my white fur on their smart black trousers. I now recognise some of these men by their smell, in my favourite group there are lots of animal smells, the young one smells of a male cat, I think he has one to look after him – he is very young; the jolly one smells of a dog, I'm getting better at recognising the smell of different breeds of dogs – and I smell poodle on him; two of the others – the father and son, have a whiff, actually it's more of an odour of Jack Russell; but one chap has a variety of smells about him, yes there is a doggy pong (and I'm guessing it's a Chihuahua), and a whiff of cat, but I can also pick up a waft of birds, part of it I recognise – chickens, well hens to be precise, but interestingly there is also something more exotic, I'm not sure what exactly, it's different, can you keep an ostrich or emu as a pet?

Then after fussing me they go back into church and come back out with the big box. Sometimes they take it straight into the churchyard and sometimes they drive it away, whatever happens the people follow the big box, I'm not exactly sure what's in it, it must be something very special, Pips pretends she knows, but she isn't letting on to me.

Week 11 - Boxes of Cardboard

I have main jobs and tasks at the Vicarage, we all do, Jasper insists on inspecting the food my human guardians try to eat. He loves his job. Beasley's job is to inspect all the shoes and boots – he must love the strange pong that permeates from them. And my favourite job is to inspect all the cardboard boxes. I love this job. We get lots of cardboard boxes at the vicarage. There are two types – the first type is those she brings home when she's been shopping, they smell of vegetables or fruit – which I guess she's eaten on her way home as they are empty. One common factor with these boxes is that they saw holes in them – for human hands to go through to carry them, or better still for cat paws to reach out of them and hit other cats (or human ankles) as they pass by – what a fantastic game that is, I call that the 'Happy Snappy Game' because I'm like a crocodile jumping out on my prey... and it's such fun to see the surprise in their unexpecting faces and that does make me rather happy.

The other type of boxes that arrive at the Vicarage have something in them. She looks almost as excited as I am when the parcel arrives but once she opens the box she then almost ignores it, rather preferring to look at what's inside. I don't mind this as generally she then takes whatever is inside the box out and leaves me the box to inspect. There is a vigorous inspection routine I must perform and this is done mainly from sitting inside the box. I need to check if there is enough room for me to sit in – is this a squeeze or comfortable? Can I stretch out and touch all the sides at once? Is it taller than me? Can I jump in and out in one leap? How does it smell? How strong is the cardboard? Is it strong enough to carry me in it? How good is it to scratch at? How tasty is it to chew, especially at the corners? And of course – how warm is it?

All very important questions, not many boxes meet my criteria to become my next new sleeping place – but I do try to give as many as possible a chance. The annoying thing is, she doesn't always realise that I've chosen a box to be my new bed, and sometimes she has the audacity to put the contents back in the box and move the box out of my way. That's not fair.  So whenever possible I do try to show her that I have selected that particular box to be mine by staying in the box. This sometimes requires serious sleeping in the box and repeatedly going back into the box when she lifts me out of it. Generally, my persistence pays off and she reluctantly moves my new prize box into the front room, placing it on the sofa so I can sleep in my new favourite box in my old favourite place. It's hard to train humans but I'm persistent and she's getting there – sometimes!

Week 12 - Metal Wheelie Boxes

Why am I strangely drawn to them? I didn't use to be, I used to be very scared indeed of the 'Metal Wheelie Boxes' especially after one clipped me and I ended up at the Vets. But I've grown in experience and confidence. I think sitting outside the Vicarage and watching them come and go has been rather therapeutic for me. The Metal Wheelie Boxes aren't trying to hurt me, rather they come along, stop, and let humans get out. Now I'm not sure if the humans are prisoners or servants of the Metal Wheelie Boxes as they do seem to rely on them rather a lot to move any distance.

At the churchyard there seems to be a ritual which most humans are observant to, the Metal Wheelie Box brings them up the church drive, slowly, then stops at the hedge, never in the hedge, but always before it. Then one or all of the people trapped inside escape slowly, walking round to the churchyard or sometimes (like on Fun-days) into the church. Then after various lengths of time, the humans return to the Metal Wheelie Box and willingly get in and then off it goes with them again.

My own guardians are also caught up in this bizarre activity. When I recognise one of their Metal Wheelie Boxes coming up the drive I run up to greet them, hoping to help them escape from its clutches and be free again – just like I'm born free, so too can they be free of these things. And it works – for a while, sometimes even a whole night passes before he has to return to his Metal Wheelie Box.

My guardians have several of these nasty creatures to care for. The most dangerous one lives in a special room just outside of the house. It's locked up most of the time, but occasionally he puts on his oily, dirty smelly overalls (which I love to curl up on when he throws them on the floor) and goes and feeds this nasty white metal box beast. I've seen him propping it up on wooden blocks, taking its wheels off it and other bits out of it and feeding it what I think is oil, well it certainly smells like oil. Sometimes he's under the beast for a long time. I remember trying to help on one occasion and as it was taking him ages I decided to have a little cat nap to pass the time. When I woke up from my slumber the air had turned cold, the room was dark, and the big metal door was shut down to the ground. 'Oh no,' I thought, 'I'm trapped in here with the sleeping metal wheelie beast,' panic struck me, and I did that thing of taking a deep breath in and then forcing it out through my mouth, sometimes after I've done that my guardian appears, but neither of them came this time. Didn't they know I was missing. Didn't they care I was trapped. And worse was to come, yes, my tummy started rumbling, I was hungry, I hadn't eaten for hours. And so with an empty tummy and cold fur I found a corner to curl up in and pray they would soon miss me, as I fell into a deep sleep.

The light in the room flickered on my eyelids and brought me quickly out of my sleep, in the haze of my drowsiness I saw the outline of his figure, with her stood behind him, they both looked worried, and he reached around the metal box to pick me up and passed me to her. How she clung on to me, cuddling me so tight I couldn't move, and for once I didn't wriggle at all, just so grateful my prayers had been answered. As they carried me into the Vicarage I could smell the aroma of tuna, my favourite, 'they had missed me after all' I thought after I'd licked my bowl clean. Prayers do get answered, we just need to be ready to see the results.

Week 13 - Taste and You Shall See

Humans do eat strange things. I know this to be a fact as I've tried various bits and pieces of their food over the years. Things I like to eat...

- Tuna – preferably in spring water, but I'll nibble at it if it's been in brine.
- Kibble (dried cat food biscuits) but only a certain type that they now have stopped selling in the shops, so my guardian has to order it via her 'cat-top', and it comes in a really big sack, in a really big box – so win win for me.
- Sachets of cat food – but only a certain subset of a certain brand, which of course is the nicest and probably not the cheapest either.
- Cat food 'mousse' – although I would love it if it was 'mouse flavoured mousse'.
- Squirty cream – now I'm very discerning, it has to be real cream and it has to be full fat, or else I'll walk off after a sniff, giving a tail flick as I go my own way.
- Crunchie Cat Treats – now I'm very fussy at home about what I like and don't like, yet over at church, it's odd but I'm not that fussy, the peaceful ambient nature of the church makes me grateful for any treats I'm offer, strange but does food taste nice in God's house?

Food that my guardians eat that I like, well certainly nothing she eats, it's generally a plateful of various leaves, occasionally there might be a little bit of cheese I fancy but hardly ever.

Whereas his plate can be more interesting but somethings smell nice – like curry, but taste dreadful. Jasper tries to inspect all his food and warns me, but Jasper likes the hot spicy meats and I certainly don't.

Other things that I enjoy eating:-
- Strands of tinsel – although this is seasonal so needs to be scoffed when available, can also be played with like spaghetti, but a warning, it may come out like it goes in, so you could have sparkly 'business'.
- Old shoe laces – great to chew, the older the better as they have a variety of tastes depending on what mud, water etc. they have stomped through when in the boots.
- Cardboard – all boxes need to be inspected and part of the testing involves me chewing a corner of the box. It's great fun and helps to keep my teeth clean.
- My guardians – well that's more licking and biting rather than eating, but there is nothing nicer after play fighting with their hand than to bite into their fur-less skin, after first licking off all the possible salt from their skin. Some areas are more salty than others, and I have to be careful as sometimes she might have put on some substance that smells artificial, that may smell flowery but tastes of chemicals – uggh. He can be even worse as he often

tastes how his old car smells – and that's not very nice at all.

Week 14 - Baptisms & Babies

Human babies are most peculiar. They smell different, they look different and are nearly as cute as me. A great deal of fuss is given to human babies, and rightly so, everyone is special. But humans do bizarre things and I've observed the 'Baby Washing' ritual.

This happens in church, generally on a Fun-day after the first service, different people arrive, generally very smartly dressed, and the women have those painful high heels on, not just painful for them to walk in but painful if they tread on my paws – hence I avoid the people at this event. Often, but not always, there are lots of children too, and there is always a baby. The baby looks cute in its white clothes – obviously they want their new born kitten to look like me, hence the white bright clothes.

This event involves everyone getting up part way through the service and gathering around the old stone bowl at the back of church, which now has its thick heavy wooden lid removed and clean warm water is in the glass bowl inside it. Once when 'helping' my guardian to set up for one of these occasions I nearly fell in when I jumped on top of the stone bowl only to find there wasn't a wooden lid on it anymore - that was a close shave.

After everyone has got up and stood by the stone structure, my guardian takes the baby off its parents and gives it a little wash, three times she pours water on its head. I'm not sure why, but it must be special as the parents don't seem to mind and just smile and nod while family and friends take lots of photographs. Maybe she is showing them how to wash the baby, but then she's not doing a very good job, she's not licked it once!

After this everyone looks happy, now the baby has been washed, and return to their seats and then shortly after that they start leaving the church. What has gone on, I don't know, maybe she's teaching them something, maybe they are coming together to celebrate something, whatever it is, everyone looks jolly happy especially my guardian, so happy, as if she's welcomed a new member into a special family. Hey ho, humans are strange.

Week 15 - Fish and Ponds

Well you would have thought I'd dragged a baby unicorn into the house by the look my guardian gave me yesterday. She looked horrified and then she started to smile as she reached for the kitchen towel, approaching me with lots of those soft absorbent squares. What was her problem? Yes I was a little wet, well completely soaking; and yes I had got a little

grass tangled on me, well actually I was covered in rather a lot of pond weed, which does have rather a strong smell to it, well actually it stinks of fish poo. But what she failed to realise is that at last I had won the game. I'd been playing 'tag' with the fish who live in the pond in our garden, it's not easy. When they see me, they swim down to the bottom of the murky water and hide, sometimes for ages. I've spent many hours sat by the pond waiting for them to come up to the top, so I can gently tap them and meow 'tag' and then the rules of the game are that they then have to chase me.

Today the edge of the pond was slippery because of the recent rain. When I saw a little goldfish come up to the surface right next to me, I couldn't resist, so without thinking my paw swiped out in front of me and into the water so I tagged it, and I did. It may have only been for a brief second, but my paw did touch it. As it shot away in surprise I felt my back paws slipping on the dampness and my front paws getting colder and wet as I slid down the side of the pond and into the cold, muddy water. The fish darted about, to my left and then to my right, it was very confusing and what only lasted a couple of seconds seemed to happen in slow motion. Quick as a flash I regained my balance and jumped quickly out of the water, bringing the various pond plants out with me. Although cold and wet and a bit smelly, I was rather pleased with myself – because all the fish ran away, none of them tagged me, so that means I won the game.

I don't think my guardian appreciated my victory, I did try to tell her but all she wanted was to pull all the weeds off me and wrap me in those squares of soft paper. Not exactly the home coming for a champion that I expected – or deserved. Once she'd finished cleaning me, she gave me lunch – tuna – perhaps she did know after all that I had beaten those sneaky slippery fish at long last.

Sometimes in life we do need to take chances, things don't always go how we expect, but I've not let that put me off trying – maybe one day I'll even get to win at tag with the squirrels.

Week 16 – Church Bells and Ropes

I do enjoy nipping into church, as so many weird and wonderful things go on in and around the historic old building. Take last Tuesday evening for example. While sat out at the front of the Vicarage I saw one big metal wheelie box pull up and then another and then another. Now that means something exciting is going to happen when there are so many of these things parked by the church. So off I go, to investigate what's about to happen and offer my help. Well the church door is left slightly ajar, so I sneak in unnoticed by the four people who now are going up the stairs at the back of the Vestry and up onto the first-floor landing.

Fascinated by them I keep watching as they stand in a line with their arms up in the air. Pips sneaks into the church too and sits next to me, seeing what I'm staring at she also looks up too. Then they each in turn pull down a big heavy rope, and when they've pulled it down they let it go again, and up shoots the heavy thick rope while they catch hold of it again and pull it down again. Pips' ears are twitching madly, I'm not sure what's happening but she's not happy and goes up to the top end of the church, settling herself in a comfy chair near the Altar. I continue to watch, thinking what a fun game they are having, but why on earth do they keep letting go of their big bit of heavy string.

After a while I decide it's time to help them more directly and I go through the Vestry and scamper up the narrow

33

twisting staircase to arrive on the first-floor landing where they are still pulling at their ropes. I can see their lips moving, so I know they are talking but my lip-reading skills are still quite poor, I can understand when my guardians say 'No' but I don't always obey them and that's about all I can make out, so all I know is that these people aren't saying 'no' to each other. Then I'm seen by the little woman – she smiles kindly, moves her lips and they all look round to see me, and some of them forget to catch and pull their ropes – whoops, it causes much laughter for them and then they carry on catching and letting go of their ropes. I try to show them the need to catch and hold their bit of string as I demonstrate this hunting technique with a bit of cord I find in a dusty corner, but they just don't seem to understand and carry on doing it their way – the wrong way.

After a time, I stroll downstairs, 'sometimes you just can't help others' I muse as I walk out of church sitting by the door. Then a kind looking old lady slowly walks down the path, I walk up to her, getting a little fuss and accompany her as she walks round to the churchyard. As I do I notice the four people leaving and locking up the building, but I can't help but wonder 'Where's Pips?'

Week 17 - Photographs & Pictures

Why do humans keep various images around their home? Some of them hang on the walls, both large and small, some feature pictures of themselves, others don't. Smaller pictures used to be placed on various flat surfaces, on window sills, on the fire place and on shelves. These were great for knocking off and I've done it to most of them, several times. Now I've noticed they have stopped replacing these pictures after I've knocked them off, I guess they understand I've won the 'Knocking Off Game' paws down and they now feel defeated.

So apart from giving me fun what else do these images do? Some are pretty to look at, some show them when they were in their kitten years, younger with various scenes behind them. I wonder if humans have poor memories, do they need to keep pictures of what they've done, where they've been and indeed even who they are? How sad that they can't just sit there thinking back to all the things they've done. I regularly do this, most of my memories are happy – hunting squirrels, wrestling with pigeons, lapping up the squirty cream, but of course I've got sad memories, being abandoned as a kitten, living at a rescue centre with over 100 other cats, all wanting a fur-ever loving home. But I try not to recall these memories too often.

I've noticed recently a couple of pictures of a cat that looks just like me has been hung on the wall. Well actually I think it is me, I've seen my reflection in both the pond and then in their special frames on the wall that reflect things back, I know these to be true because it doesn't just show me but it also shows my guardian who is holding me. Both my guardians waste time looking into these special frames, but not together, he does it in the bathroom, especially when trying to get the cream off his face – but he put it there just a few minutes ago, and she does it when she's trying on different fur to go out in.

Beasley the kitten saw his reflection for the first time and hissed at it while arching his back, he thought it was another cat, kittens are silly, I never did that, or did I, time I think to sit and recall some of my kitten memories. It's never a bad thing to be with your happy memories, they can help shape a happy future too.

Week 18 - Brushing Teeth

The more I observe my human guardians the more confused I become. Take for example their rituals of morning and evenings. They take off night fur and put on day fur and vice versa in the evening. But there is something else I've observed they do around this time every day – well twice a day. He does it in the bathroom, she does it as she walks around the house. What are they doing? Well let me explain more. It involves a little thin stick with bristles at one end. He puts some white gunk on it and then, rather than eating it, he puts it under the tap – possibly to drown it, as he uses lots and lots of water, and then swivels it around his mouth lots of times, it must be putting up a bit of a fight as he ends up with lots of foam around his mouth and guess what then – he spits it out in the sink! How disgusting is that?

She does the same but uses just a drop of water, and her stick thing with bristles at the end lights up, she doesn't get foam around her mouth, but she also spits it out. What are they doing? If their breath smells (like Jasper's does) then they should try chewing catmint. Catmint is lovely, not only does the smell of it make me happy but when I chew a leaf or two or three off the bush it makes me relax and feeling a giggly happiness with the world. I love catmint. Or perhaps it's not their breath, but rather they want to clean their teeth, well once more they could learn from me, how do I clean my teeth? Simple, I chew long grass in the garden, it has a bittersweet taste and helps to keep my teeth clean and sharp – no messing around with foam everywhere or wasting precious water. Really you humans could learn so much from us cats.

Week 19 - Newspapers & Cat Naps

Cats need to be warmer than humans, that's a fact. I need to find the best places to sleep, to snooze or to just sit and watch. This takes a lot of discernment, depending on the weather, the season, the wind and so much more. Each cat is unique and finds places that suit them best. In the summer Jasper likes the cool shade by the pond – I think it is so he can also lap up the fishy water in it. Nipper will lay on the bed while the sun is shining on it, then in the evenings he sprawls out across the paving slabs, which are still warm from the sunshine.

My favourite places vary. After breakfast I like to stroll around the churchyard and neighbouring close. Then for my morning nap you will often find me sleeping in the middle of the stairs. If anyone or any cat comes up or down the stairs I can feel the movement and it wakes me up. This way Beasley the kitten cannot playfully jump on me, nor can Hissy Missy sneak up on me either. After lunch I will then have my afternoon nap in the office where my guardian works. She placed a wicker basket on top of the filing cabinet, and she must have meant it for me because it's got newspapers in it. I love newspapers, there is nothing better than curling up on a pile of newspapers, except of course walking across one while they are trying to read it. I'll curl up in my basket that she has so lovingly prepared just for me, and guess what, each week she adds another newspaper to the pile.

One day it will be full, I'm not sure where I'll have my afternoon nap then.

But what about my post-teatime nap, in the summer this is with Jasper out by the pond, I hide under the shade of the plants, so I can jump out on Missy, playing an impromptu game of 'Happy Snappy' which she hates, because I win it. Sometimes I'm not alone in my hiding place but on several occasions I've found a frog there too, well when I take this unexpected gift to my humans I do get the most bizarre reaction – she looks petrified and then tries to find him. He looks kind and I think wants to share the frog with me, so takes it off me, but rather than playing with it, he puts it back in the pond. Well I guess I'll still have the fun of catching it again.

For my post-supper nap I generally have this in the front room, on the sofa. This is brilliant if they have left a newspaper there and then to make it comfier I have to shred it a little with my claws and rip it a little with my teeth. And then I can settle down for the night, it's often the simplest things in life that give me the most pleasure.

Week 20 - The Cat's Whiskers

In my observations I've come to notice more and more humans are trying to copy us cats, although not doing a great job. One particular thing I've noticed is how the males of the species are growing their whiskers. But they've got it wrong. Their whiskers start off fine, growing out of their face as they should do, they don't need to be on their chins or above their upper lip, but if that's their choice fair enough. And then it goes wrong, rather than growing a cheek-full either side that grow horizontally, they are growing a face-full that grows downwards, vertically. They are pretty much useless.

My whiskers are amazing, not only do they help me to communicate with other cats but I learn so much more about the natural environment I'm out and about exploring. My whiskers go deeper than my other fur, so they are far more sensitive at detecting any change, such as the slightest change in direction of the breeze. I've also got whiskers in my eyebrows, under my chin and behind my front paws – mind you I have noticed odd strands of hair growing in strange places on the older humans who come to church – maybe they are trying to be more cat-like too.

I can use my whiskers to judge if I'm going to fit through a hole or not. However, common sense is still needed, after all when Jasper was at his fattest his whiskers didn't grow that much, he could have got stuck in lots of things if he wasn't careful. And of course, if my whiskers are pointing forward, that means I'm alert and could be getting ready to pounce on anything that moves.   If I see Beasley the kitten with his whiskers pointing forward, it usually means he's getting ready to pounce – on me!   Kittens have so much energy and so little common sense, I'm sure I wasn't like that when I was his age!

Week 21 - Weddings in My Church

Spring has sprung, and Summer is just around the corner. Fantastic! For me there is nothing better than finding a safe, sunny spot and having a little cat nap, or even a long cat nap, except for having a squirty cream treat. Well in addition to the longer warmer days, I've noticed something else that seems to happen more often at the church when the weather gets warmer.

Now this special worship usually happens on 'Cat-urday, but not always. My guardian goes to open the church, and various people start to join her, I don't recognise these people but generally they are friendly to me as I slink in-between them, getting a bit of fuss from a few standing around. A 'pawful' of them stand around putting some sort of stick thing into their mouth then taking it out again, and they keep repeating this activity; really, they should make their minds up if they want it between their lips or not! Now I do need to keep a watchful eye for those women in high heels, they often are a little wobbly and I'm scared of those pointy heels treading on my little paws. Then the smartly dressed people go inside the church and leave my guardian waiting outside as a shiny, clean car arrives with ribbons on its bonnet, I love playing with ribbons, but even I sense I'm not allowed to with these ribbons.

Then out of the car steps a beautiful lady, accompanied by several other friends. The woman generally wears a bright white stunning dress – I think they are honouring me, and trying to copy my bright white fur, after all imitation is the greatest form of flattery. Why else would she wear such a special dress? Well the woman in her 'Florence dress' follows my guardian into the church with her friends following her. Everyone looks so happy, it's such a lovely occasion.

After a while, long enough for me to have a short cat nap, they all come out again, led by the woman in white and a smartly dressed man. They look so overjoyed, they often forget to notice me. At each service there is a different couple, but each time the woman wears a special dress, that always seems to be white, I've never seen a woman coming out in a dress that's the same colour as Pips' fur. Then lots of people gather round the couple on the grass and throw lots of tiny pieces of paper at them, but they miss and it flutters around in the wind, that looks such fun to chase them but the couple just stand in the middle smiling with the paper fluttering past them. People are strange!

Week 22 - Touch & Touching

Most cats are rather sensitive in some ways. I'm really sensitive to touch. It doesn't mean I'm stand off-ish but it does mean I only want touching when and where I want to be touched, and with the pressure or degree that I find acceptable.

Take for instance my guardian brushing my fur. Sometimes I love it, sometimes I hate it. This firstly depends on what brush she is using. The pink one causes my fur to get statically charged. It's not fun having one's fur full of static and getting shocks as you go about your daily duties. The purple brush is far better, its metal teeth drag through my fur, taking out all the loose fur, and that feels lovely, leaving me feeling lighter and brighter but sometimes she can do it rather enthusiastically, I hate that as she drags it too fast and that pulls my skin a bit too much, making me turn and bite the hand that is brushing me. She looks hurt when I bite her but how else can I explain to her to stop it. Then there is the yellow comb with the narrow plastic teeth, this also glides through my fur removing any bits of dirt or grit I may have just happened to roll in. I like this, but only for a short time, so again have to communicate with her by biting her hand to tell her it is time to stop.

One of my favourite types of touch is when she strokes me – but again not just anytime or anywhere but when I'm stretched out and sleeping on the sofa or in the sunshine, then it adds to the feeling of joy as she gently fusses me. This reminds me of being a kitten and how much mum used to wash me with her rough sandpaper-like tongue. I miss my mum, so it's nice to be reminded of her by my guardians.

Now one of my favourite types of touch is when I touch her, this can be done in various places and various ways, I think she really likes it when I surprise her. Often she is engrossed by the sink, cleaning my cat bowls with the bubbly water (why, I've licked it clean) and I come and rub myself against her legs and then squeeze between her ankles. Generally she looks down smiling, but if she doesn't realise I'm there then I do my favourite thing, I stretch up as far as I can and put my front paws, with claw out, into her leg, often my sharp little claws prick through the denim fabric and directly into her skin. Gosh she definitely knows I'm there and I get her attention quickly. Touch is so important for us cats, I'm pleased my training of her is getting some results!

Week 23 - Prayer & Meditation

Well it's not that hot yet to be called 'flaming June' but when it does get a bit too warm guess where I like to go to cool down – inside the church. It's so cool in there, it's like medieval air-conditioning in the summer months. And it just so happened the other day I saw my guardian going into the church with Pips the tabby cat dutifully following her, so I trotted in behind them. Once inside Pips and I started to play 'tag' – this basically involves her running under the pews and me chasing her and me then hitting her (gently) when I've caught her, then she chases me and so the game continues. However, we soon got out of breath and I thought we should play 'Hide and Seek', so off I went and hid under the organ – it's great under there, no one else goes there and it's full of dust and cobwebs and smells musty.

Well, when at first they didn't find me I thought 'How clever am I' but then the sun started to drop in the sky and I knew time was passing and still they hadn't found me. I ventured out of my hiding place (okay I had a little nap first) to find the church empty, they had gone and the door was closed. A game of 'Hide and Seek' should last 5 to 10 minutes but this now had gone on for a couple of hours. Oh, I was angry with them, why did they leave me here on my own, why didn't Pips come and find me, she's been good at that in the past. So, I stretched my legs and had a walk around the church. Then I sat looking at the big stained glass window. I'd seen it before but never really looked at it. With the setting sun, the colours were so bright, I could see clearly the pictures, each image telling a story, a story of God's love and God in action in the world – well God could do another action I selfishly thought as the church was beginning to feel cold on my paws, and it was past my tea time, so once again in a time of need I found myself praying for God to help me.

I'm not sure how long I sat there in prayer and in mindfulness meditation - not so much as looking at the windows but looking into them, and reflecting on the different Bible stories they portrayed. Then I saw the lights come on – literally – she was back, when I saw her I ran to her and let her pick me up, she was warm

and soft, I couldn't help but purr with joy. After eating a large supper, I thought about my time in church – life is busy, how often do we willingly make time to stop, to pray and to listen to God at work in our lives and hearts. Sometimes we need to make the time or God may do it for us in unexpected ways – like a game of 'Hide and Seek' lasting 7 hours!

Week 24 - Clothes

So okay I wasn't the cleanest I'd ever been, but there was no need for such a dramatic reaction from my guardian. It had been a hot summer's day and how to cool off was a bit of an issue for me. Now I now my humans wear different fur – whoops I mean clothes, depending on what the season is and what the weather is like – but us cats have the same fur day in and day out. Yes, during the Spring and Summer I may moult more and have my lightweight summer coat, and in the Autumn and Winter I grow a thicker coat to protect me from those cold winds but generally it's pretty much the same.

So why don't humans learn from us cats, they have such rituals around what clothes to where and when. After getting up she changes out of her night clothes and into her day clothes. The night clothes and the clothes from previous days are put into a wicker basket – that is such fun to scratch, but I have to do that when she's not looking or else I get a wiggly finger pointed at me. And then after a day or two she bundles them into the spinny machine (because it spins everything around – I have watched it on a few occasions but it's not as interesting as the changing picture box) and they go into it dry and come out soaking wet. Why she couldn't just lick them clean like I do with my fur is beyond me, it seems far easier and far less fuss. And that's not the end of it, after draping them over an indoor rack – which is no fun to climb, she then flattens them with the hissy steamy thing.

He seems far more sensible in his routines to me. Most nights he leaves his clothes on the floor in the bedroom and when she is not around he will often put them on again the following morning. He is simpler, less time and less fuss. Again before they go out in the evenings – he's changing his clothes in minutes but she is still running backwards and forwards looking anxious as she tries on several different sets of clothes. What difference does it make, as long as you don't get too hot or too cold what does it really matter. Does the span of your life increase by such worrying – no!

Week 25 - Hens & Pigeons

I know they are a bit bigger than most birds, but I do enjoy playing with the hens in the garden. Why? Well because they don't cheat at chase. The other birds, especially the pigeons, cheat and fly away when I get close to them. The hens don't fly off, they do flap their wings and run around the garden. It's so entertaining, they run into the bushes and then run out, scattering everywhere, so I have to single one of them out to chase - generally I choose the colourful little cockerel to focus on. He hates it, but it's so funny. I never hurt him, I think I could catch him but playing the game is sometimes more important than winning. And if I won I doubt he would want to play the game and chase me, I think he just wants to scratch around in the soil looking for bugs.

But the hens can be helpful, not by giving me a hand with my jobs around the Vicarage - such as the Box Inspector, but rather when I'm trying to hunt the pigeons. Because the hens also enjoy eating the bird seed my guardian leaves out every morning, so while they are scoffing the seed other birds come and join them. This means I can get really close to the pigeons. Indeed, one day last week as a feathery friend was busy filling its beak I was able to creep up behind him, pounce and grab him. I held onto his tail with my paws. He struggled trying to get away, so I put my paws around him, but he was rather big and heavy, and I lost my balance but still clung onto him, gently sticking my claws into his feathery torso. So, it became a bit of a wrestling match. As he tried to escape he pulled me to the left, as I regained my balance I pulled him to the right, and so it became more of a dance as we wriggled together on the soft green lawn. Well it seemed to last for hours but probably only a minute or two before he gathered all his energy and pulled away and flew into the trees.

There I lay on the grass, out of breath and in shock. What a fun game, I'm sure I won but I must express – pigeons are cheats!

Week 26 – A Summer Night Out

Yes! I did it! Did what? For the first time in many years – well since the incidents of 'playing' with a neighbours' cat, at 2am under her guardians' bed, and my glorious winning of that game of 'tag' as she cowered under their bed, since then I've been grounded every night. But last night I did it and cunningly evaded my guardians (or jailors) and got to spend the whole night outside.

It was a wonderful night. The day had been a scorcher, I'd spent most of it asleep in the shade of a bush with a gentle breeze. In the evening it was a little cooler, and I had lots of energy. The last thing I wanted to do was spend the night shut in the front room. So I hid behind the fence near the church. I saw her come out looking for me, but I wanted her to know I was okay so ran out and danced in-between her legs. As she bent down to scoop me up, I quickly nipped away under a parked car. She stomped back in the house and then came out again, with him. He brought an old piece of string, normally I love chasing string, but oh no, not this time I thought, knowing if I chased the string with him, then she'd pick me up when I was distracted – how unfair is that. After a while they both went back in and came back out with my cat bowl. The smell of tuna gently wafted in the warm air. Normally I would run out and scoff it up as quickly as possible, but I'd already eaten so could resist this fishy temptation.

I'm so pleased I did, as they went in and I was left out. Out to explore the night time. Gosh things are different in the dark. The moon lit up the night sky, without a cloud in the heavens thousands of stars shined so brightly. Guess what – lots of other animals come out at

night, the shy fox came out of the undergrowth and played in the churchyard with her cubs, I think she was teaching them 'Hide and Seek' among the graves. The bats circle around the church tower catching flies and bugs to eat. The owl sat on the tree branch observing what was happening while keeping an eye out for a plump little mouse or two. As did I but without any luck. All the mice must have gone early to their beds. Night time is beautiful, things look different, night time is great to explore hedges and climb trees.

As the dawning sun spread across the morning sky, I went back home. For a special treat I bounced into my guardians' bedroom, jumping on their bed I meowed with all my breath, which promptly woke them up. They looked so pleased to see me, but it took a bit more jumping on them before she got up to give me my breakfast – well I was hungry – after all I'd missed my tuna supper.

Week 27 – Foxy Florence & The Chase

Well I never. Well actually I did and it's doing it that made everyone panic. So let me begin by saying it was a lovely Summer's evening and I was sat on the warm paving slabs enjoying the sun's energy that they had been absorbing all day, and now slowly releasing, keeping me nice and warm. And then I saw him, he was under the apple tree sniffing around. He was long, thin, lean and with a fluffy bush of a tail, with his reddish brown fur looking rather dull and matt. Yes, it was the largest squirrel I'd ever seen. He was so big, I'd never seen a squirrel that big before. So without a second thought I went into action and ran straight at him. Immediately as I moved my first paw he spotted me and started to run into the bushes, so I ran as quick as my paws could carry me towards him, he shot off round the bush, so I doubled back on myself to try to intercept his cunning moves. And then as I got close he put on a sprint, as I reached out to touch his fluffy tail he quickened his pace and then leapt over the fence in one huge jump and was out of the garden. As I stopped in amazement at the speed and size and agility of this squirrel I saw my guardian coming running out of the house, picking me up and cuddling me rather tightly. Well I have no chance of catching up with that big squirrel I thought as I wriggled in her arms, pretending I didn't like her cuddles.

Later that same evening, after I'd had my fishy supper I nuzzled up to her on the sofa, as she tapped away at her 'cat-top' (because cats like to sit on top of them when we can't sit on our human's lap) and saw a picture on her cat -top of a similar squirrel to the big one in the garden I'd been chasing, only to learn it wasn't a squirrel after all, but rather it was a fox! I should have known by the smell, I've often smelt foxes in our garden, and seen them in the distance but this fox was so close. So now I know what a fox looks like close up, I do hope Mr Fox visits us again, I enjoyed playing chase with him, maybe next time I'll catch up with him and win the game.

Week 28 – The Changing Picture Box

As the sun sets in the sky another light comes on in the Vicarage most evenings. This indoor light thingy is dull in the day time but when he sits down with his evening meal on a tray on his lap the dull box in the corner of the front room springs to life with a variety of changing and moving pictures on it. It seems to me the moving pictures fall into three categories.

1. Black and white moving pictures, these often are of people, looking rather stifled in their movements and expressions, at some point there will be moving pictures of planes, I would chase them but they just aren't very interesting, and then there seems to be scenes of happiness at the end, a triumph of some sort.

2. These are colour moving pictures, the centre of the focus is on some sort of vehicle, starting off rusty and missing bits and ending up shiny and sparkling, with the grumpy men who were tinkering with it now standing around looking happy and proud. He does like these programmes, perhaps it's because they wear dirty greasy overalls like he does.

3. These are my favourite moving pictures – the nature programmes, oh I do love to watch them all. It might be big cats in Africa, or whales in the blue sea or anything, I love them all and do admit sometimes I get carried away, jumping up in front of the 'Moving Picture Box' to get a closer look, practising my hunting skills and hitting the animals before they move off the

screen. Sometimes my guardians actually come and move me away, I'm not sure why, it's not as if they want to practise their hunting skills.

Recently they put on a special moving picture just for me, well since they put it on and then go to bed, leaving me on my own in the front room I'll assume that it is just for me. On this moving picture is everything I love – close up movies of pigeons, squirrels, mice, little birds and the list goes on. I love watching it as I fall to sleep, having lots of dreams about playing chase with the little mice. Happy dreams!

Week 29 - The Churchyard

Living at the Vicarage is a great privilege. I've lived at three Vicarages now, I do enjoy the attention I get from visitors and the fun of having such a large garden to run across but the best thing has to be the churchyard. I love the churchyard. I'm not sure exactly what else goes on there but I love it for all the games we cats can play. The easiest game is 'Hide and Seek', one of us will go and hide behind a gravestone and then wait to be found. I've tried to teach this simple game to my humans but when she comes down with me in the evenings she just sits on the bench, thinking. She doesn't even try to hide, it's obvious where she is sitting, any cat can see her. Then I try to show her the other part, by going and hiding, but when she walks back up the path, she cheats by walking upright and can see over the tops of the gravestones. 'Hide and Seek' is no fun with her. So now I only play with other cats, I used to play with George but he now prefers to go into the church, where Pips is and they get fuss off the people sat inside.

Darwin is more fun, and as well as playing 'Hide and Seek' we play 'Chase Me' along the path, this really just involves us taking it in turns to run fast in a straight-ish line along the path – hence the name. An added bonus is when one of us catches up with the other and then jumps over them and into the lead, we have to be quick or else we end up in the prickly hedge. Whoops.

Sometimes I sit and watch the people in the churchyard, they don't seem happy when they come in, often they have pretty flowers that smell fantastic, but then they leave them on the granite plaques and gravestones, I'm not exactly sure what is underneath them, but it must be something very important to leave such colourful flowers to wither away on that spot. Often, I will go and introduce myself to these unhappy visitors, they generally give me a bit of fuss and a gentle smile, but I've noticed they seem to have tears in their eyes. Why? Are they allergic to the flowers? Maybe that's why they leave them behind.

Week 30 - Cat Carriers

Somethings, well most things my human guardians get wrong, completely wrong, like hunting, and eating and sleeping. Occasionally they do have a good idea. One such good idea was to have lots of snuggle places around the Vicarage. I love sleeping and I love sleeping inside boxes and baskets, especially off the ground, so I'm out of the way from cold draughty floors and where no other cat can pounce on me. There are various sleeping boxes and baskets. Some are made from cardboard and have newspaper in the bottom of them for me to scratch before settling down to snooze. Some are plastic with a roof and a little door to go in. Often these have an old tea towel to snuggle in and some are made from wicker, which are great to pad in and nibble at the bits poking through.

They place the boxes in nice spots too, where the sun shines in the morning, so I can get warm first thing. Others are put close to the window so I can use it as a hide when watching the pigeons. And for my night time slumber a cardboard box can be found on the sofa – well what's a sofa without a box on it – my guardians don't need that much space after all.
It's odd how sometimes one of the plastic boxes will disappear briefly, and then re-appear but with a slightly different smell – a whiff of the clinical cleanness found at the vets. I'll never forget that smell. It's almost like they are leaving the baskets and boxes out so we cats get used to sleeping in them, so then when one of us has to go to the vets

it's less traumatic because we are going in a carrier that is familiar and comforting to us.

Well while I was pondering this concern the other day, Jasper walked past me, and as I realised I hadn't seen him for the past hour, wondering where he had been, my nostrils filled with the unique smell of the vets. Both Jasper and the basket had not only gone missing at the same time but also smelt of the vets – just a coincidence or is something going on? I'm not sure but I shall be keeping a watchful eye on my human guardians in future.

Week 31 - The Fantastic Fridge

I'm not sure if magic really exists, but if it does, I think I've seen it. It stands in the Kitchen, tall, silvery grey, cold and never moving. Until one of my guardians approaches it, then instantly the tall long door opens and light beams out from it, showing how (magically) the shelves inside it are full of food. The reason I'm not sure it's magic, is because a lot of the food I don't like – who wants a bowl full of green leaves, or chilled vegetables to peel and boil. However, what can be found in there sometimes is magical.

Generally, a faint hint of chicken can be sniffed when the door comes ajar Beasley the kitten loves chicken, I think he's addicted to it as he follows our guardians as they walk to the fridge and then as they open the door, quick as a flash he's got his head inside – just a whisker away from the chicken and his paw is already touching the packet, trying to knock it out.   That kitten is so  cheeky. Jasper also hangs around, trying to inspect the food that has slipped him by, while Missy and Nipper sit under the table hoping for a pinch of grated cheese as a treat. For myself I can take or leave chicken and cheese, but there is one treat in the fabulous fridge I adore. My guardian will get a bowl or plate then squirt some lovely cold creamy stuff into it and I scoff it up straight away. Yes, it's similar to cream but more airy and lighter, and it melts on my warm tongue. Jasper also likes this squirty treat, as do Missy and Nipper and now Beasley has decided he likes it too. Honestly, I have to be quick to make sure I get my treats in the Vicarage, sometimes I think there are too many cats in my home!

Week 32 - George & Darwin

There are many cats in my home. I have a big extended family of cats here at the Vicarage, spanning from young Beasley the ginger Kitten, to old Tessa who is older than the number of claws I have, and rarely gets off her bed. I'm not allowed to play with old Tessa and old Scarlet, apparently I'm too rough and upset them, I think it's just because I win every game with them, whether it's 'Hide and Seek' or 'Happy Snappy' – I win and they hide to avoid losing.

So with a Vicarage full of adopted brothers and sisters you'd think I wouldn't need any new friends. But nothing could be further from the truth. In our current home I've made lots of friends. Archie is a sleek handsome black cat, he lives on the neighbouring close, we both sit out the front of the Vicarage and watch people going by. George used to be my best friend, he's very handsome, he's ginger and white with long hair, we were special friends and would 'hang out' together in the churchyard playing 'Hide and Seek'. Yes, I have lots of my family of cats to hang out with, but it was special with George, he didn't have to come and see me, he chose to be with me, and that made me feel special. When we played I always won, of course, but it was fun playing. Now George plays with my adopted sister Pips, they both like going into church and strolling around all the congregation getting fuss. The more fuss they get the happier they are, I try really hard not to be jealous when I see them so happy together.

But then as George and Pips spent more and more time together, it meant George wasn't hanging out with his brother Darwin. So Darwin used to sneak into our garden and practise his hunting skills with the pigeons and squirrels. I enjoy practising my hunting skills, so over a few days we got closer and now we both regularly sit together under a bush waiting for the squirrels to come down from the trees to gather and eat the peanuts, or for the fat pigeons to land and devour them too. I like Darwin, unlike George he's not bothered about getting fuss from people, he's just happy to play and hunt. Is Darwin my boyfriend – well let's say we enjoy being together, and that's enough for now.

Week 33 - Office Helper

I do try to be helpful, but sometimes it just goes all wrong. Take yesterday as a prime example. She was in and out of her room with the desk, chair and cat-top, rushing around like a kitten chasing its tail. So I thought, 'How can I help her, perhaps to slow down and relax a little?'. Then as she was ignoring me and tapping away on the cat-top, ignoring me as I sat right beside her and more importantly ignoring the packet of cat treats in-between us, so I did it, I just pushed the packet a little and it fell off the table onto the floor. She noticed me then, and grumpily picked up the packet and put it back in the same place, without even giving me a single treat or any fuss. What did I do? I did it again, one swift strike with my paw and the packet tumbled onto the floor again, but this time the packet fell open and the yummy biscuits scattered a little on the floor, she looked at me, with not a kind look, and got out of her chair and started to pick up the packet and its spilled contents. While she was busy doing that, I nipped over and sat in the swirly chair. A second or two later she looked up at me in her chair, again not a happy look, but this time put a few cat treats just where I was sat before. Didn't she realise I'd moved into her warm chair now, give me the cat treats here. So reluctantly I moved out of the big chair and back to where I'd been sat on the table before, so I could scoff the treats before any of the other cats joined me.

But once I'd eaten the treats I was soon bored again and she wasn't giving me any attention or fuss. I looked around the table and saw an elastic band – now these are a rarity, so I patted it with my paw and then started to chew it, elastic bands are such fun, but when she saw this she forcibly took it out of my mouth – and gave me a couple of cat treats instead. Not much of a swap but I still ate them. Boredom returned so I looked a little further down the table and saw the gizmo she used to attached papers together, it's black and shiny and with two taps of my paw it fell off the table, onto the floor, splitting open and a long strip of the little metal bits broke up into several pieces. She looked rather miffed at this, stopping her tapping on the cat-top, nearly getting out of her chair, but then looking at me and wheeling the chair to where the mess was, and clearing it up and then wheeling herself back. No cat treats were forthcoming at all. So how else could I help her? Aha, I spied an open box of paper clips, shiny and new, so I took a couple of steps to them, and with one paw knocked them to near the edge of the desk, she turned round and glared at me, so I pushed them again, now they were just a whisker away from the edge, I could see her lips move, and her hand reach out, but it was too late my little paw gave one firm tap and the box cascaded to the floor with those little shiny clips tumbling all across the floor. Whoops I thought, now I've done it, but rather than wagging her figure at me, she actually laughed, picked me up and took me into the kitchen and gave me some of my favourite kibble biscuits. Why didn't she just do this before. Honestly - humans I'll never understand them! Sometimes you need to stop doing so much to realise what's important in your life – like fussing me!

Week 34 - Cattery Prisons

I hate it. I can sense when it's happening. There are tell-tale signs. The first sign is that he gets the big cases out of the loft and puts them in the bedroom that they don't sleep in but where she hangs all the wet clothes until they are dry. They smell musty like the loft. The next step is that she puts the big cases onto the bed and leaves them open so they don't smell quite so musty anymore. The third step is that Pippin then goes and sleeps in one of the big cases, so it smells more of her than the loft. My guardian smiles affectionately when she sees Pippin asleep in the big case, I don't know why, I'm cuter that Pippin.

The next step is filling the big cases, not with more cats but with those wet clothes, once they are dried and flattened with that hot hissing, steamy thing that she runs backwards and forwards across their clothes. She doesn't look that happy when doing this, if you don't enjoy it, then don't do it – that's my motto. Then when the big cases are full she closes the lid on them and then I know it's going to happen. I hate it. She and he then conspire to trap me, it's at different times but I can tell because they don't let me go outside like normal. Then they put me into a carrier and put me into the car. Once Jasper must have been naughty, as he came to cat prison with me too, but last time it was me on my own. It was dreadful.

After a short car ride in their Metal Wheelie Box I was there. It smelt dreadfully of dogs and disinfectant – and despair. I hated it, they took me into a small narrow cell and after a few minutes and a few tears from her, they closed the door and left me there. I don't know what I'd done wrong. When Jasper came with me it was better, he smelt of home and that was comforting, we could snuggle together. He was as scared as me. I didn't want to be there, I wanted to be back at home, sleeping on the sofa and sitting in the garden. This was horrific. What had I done that was so bad that I had to come to prison? What was I guilty of? When did I have a trial? And how long was my sentence this time?

Well it seemed like weeks but after several days and nights had passed I saw them again - they had come back for me. Gosh how my heart pounded when I saw them walking up the corridor to me. I took a deep breath and pushed it all out of my mouth quickly - I think that's how a meow is made. And she hugged and squeezed me like she never wanted to let go of me and I didn't wriggle at all as I never wanted her to let go of me either. But after a few minutes she did let go of me and put me back in my carrier and he picked me up, smiling lots and took me into the Metal Wheelie Box and after a short ride I was released back into my lovely, wonderful home with all the other cats.

But this time when the big cases appeared it was different. Her brother appeared. I like him, he sits a lot, watching the 'Moving Picture Box', he gives me meat from his sandwiches and gently strokes me as I stretch out on the sofa next to him. It wasn't until the morning that I noticed it was her brother feeding us, my guardians had disappeared, so had the big cases, but I was still in my home, with my toys, with my family and friends. And so after several days and nights had passed they returned, looking happy but tired and the big case full of smelly clothes. She looked pleased to see me and cuddled me so tight, but why, I was fine, her brother was now fully trained in how to share his food with me – and the others. I think she was a bit sad that I didn't make more of a fuss of her – after all we all like being fussed, so when she sat down I did jump onto her lap, to let her know I had missed her, but not that much.

Week 35 – Bags

Sometimes the simplest of things in life can give me the most fun. She seems to take a bag full of stuff with her every time she leaves the house. I do enjoy squeezing myself into small places and nestling down for a snooze. So when she's not looking I spy her bag on the floor, sneakily go and paw open the top so I can jump inside and hide. Surely, what would give her more pleasure than seeing me as one of the things in her bag full of stuff? So far I've been rumbled every time I've tried, it's almost like when she picks it up she can feel my dainty body inside. Actually I'm not as dainty as I used to be, good living and a good home have meant over the past couple of years I have filled out a little, gone is my slim kitten figure and now I have a little bulging tummy. I noticed this increase in my weight when I was trying to climb a tree to get to a squirrel a couple of weeks ago – I was huffing and puffing far sooner than I used to. Maybe it's middle age creeping up on me.

But back to the bags. I've had more success in sleeping in shopping bags – the great big ones they bring back full of cat food and other food – not sure why they still buy food I don't like, maybe it's for them. Anyhow, these bags are big and easy to crawl into. And once inside no nasty drafts or cold breezes can fluff my fur up. I enjoy a snooze in a bag. But again, they don't seem to care and when they find me they lift up the bag by its handles and carry me to another part of the house, smiling as they do and he often spins the bag around in circles, so when I climb out of the bag I'm a little dizzy and have to wobble my way out, they are giggling but I don't think it's funny, it's certainly not dignified.

Then there are the best bags – paper bags, I love a big brown paper bag to snuggle in. As well as being a great place for a snooze they make great dens and ace to jump out on other cats when playing 'Happy Snappy'. But frustratingly these bags don't seem to last long, and soon get chewed, scratched and ripped, they just don't make them like they used to do!

Week 36 - Vets Visits

I'm a fit, active and healthy little cat. Yes I know I'm different to the other cats but I don't let it stop me going out and about. But I did experience a nasty accident a few years ago. While I was crossing a quiet road on my way back home, thinking about what tasty treat I could have for tea, one of those big metal wheelie boxes came out of nowhere and clipped me before I could run out of its path. Using all the adrenalin I had I ran home and hid behind the sofa and started to tremble in pain and fear. And then I feel asleep, I'm not sure how long it was but I felt the sofa being pulled away to see both my guardians looking concerned as they looked at me. Gently she bent over and delicately picked me up. My body ached and I took a sharp breath in and expelled quickly – I think that's called meowing – and she looked more concerned. He touched my front paw and the pain of that shot through me and I found myself doing that expelling air thing again and again. The next thing I knew I was being put into one of the cat carriers and then into the Metal Wheelie Box.

I was still in a daze as I was carried into the building with that unique smell – a mixed of clinical cleanliness and fearful dogs and scared cats. But I was in too much pain to care or notice as my front paw throbbed and swelled with pain and my whole body ached and trembled.

In a small room I was gently taken out of the box and a kind woman in a white coat looked into my eyes, and mouth, felt my tummy and bladder and then looked at my throbbing paw. Being deaf I'm not sure of their conversation but they seemed to look a little happier and the next thing I knew I was having a sharp prick in my fur but then felt a gentle warmth spreading through my body and numbing the pain. Everything went hazy and I'm not really sure what happened next or how long I was asleep for. But on awakening I was in a different place, it was a small cage, but different to 'holiday prison' cages. There was a young man with a kind looking face smiling at me and stroking me. And then I began to realise my front paw that had been causing me so much pain after being clipped by that nasty fast-moving metal wheelie box was now numb and wrapped in a huge thick bandage. I wanted to shake it off, it felt odd, but I just didn't seem to have any energy to do it, so just lay there, letting the nice man fuss me as I drifted back into sleep.

On waking again, I saw my guardians, oh I was so happy and wobbled as I stood up to greet them from my cage, her face was smiling but her eyes were rather red, like she'd been crying. And soon I was being gently picked up and back into my familiar smelling cat carrier. After a little time with them and the woman in the white coat all around me, I was carried back to the car and then after a short drive I was back in the Vicarage. I was so pleased to be back in my front room.

A bowl of tuna (my favourite) was placed in front of me and both he and she watched me scoff it up with smiling faces. With a full tummy I decided to have a little wash, but also couldn't really wash myself as I realised not only had I got a huge bandage on my paw but also around my tummy, stopping me from wriggling by ribs or sudden movements such as running or jumping. Gosh this was frustrating but at least I wasn't in pain like before. Off I drifted back into sleep while she gently stroked me. I really don't like going to the vets but so glad they did take me.

Week 37 - Sofas and Chairs

After sleeping, sitting is probably how I spend most of my time. Hence it's critically important where I sit, as I may decide to also have a little cat nap there too. I've been observing my guardians. They are rather limited in where, when and how they sit. I rarely see them sitting on the floor. If one of them has done that, then it seems they need the

help of a nearby table to stand up again. Sometimes, when eating at the dining room table they sit round the table, but this is getting rarer, most commonly they sit on the sofas.

This has advantages and disadvantages for me. I don't like sharing my sofa with other cats, I've got there first – hence it's mine until I leave it. But Jasper struggles to understand this and often comes to join me, thinking I want his company. Jasper is my big adopted brother, but that doesn't mean I want to share my sofa with him. His breath smells of fish, from drinking the fishy tasting water in the pond. So generally if he tries to come onto my sofa I do tap him on the whiskers, which if my guardians see, then gets me into trouble and I get pushed off the sofa by them, and Jasper takes my warm spot, life's not fair.

If I join one of my guardians on the sofa, then this is acceptable. I can choose to snuggle up to them when it's cold or take up the rest of the room and stretch out if I'm a bit hot. I love doing this as then I can push my legs onto them, and feel safe, it's so comforting knowing that they are there, and all is at rest in the Vicarage. However, I don't like it when I'm on the sofa first and they come and join me. First, whichever one it is doesn't matter because the fact is they are heavier than me, considerably heavier in fact. When they park their bottom on the sofa the first thing that happens is that the sofa squashes under their enormous weight and I'm now sliding down a bit. Secondly, they've probably either pushed me along, so they can have more room, or they've actually sat on part of me – usually my tail. I hate it when they join me on the sofa.

However, there is hope, I've learnt a tactic and that is to look cute – if I roll over onto my back and gently blink at them, I look so cute that they cannot move me and have to go and sit on the other sofa. It's great being cute!

Week 38 - Children & Babies

Small humans confuse me, I like them, but I don't understand them. Sorry I don't mean small, I mean young human, they confuse me. Take for instance a couple of days ago, there I was sitting outside of the Vicarage, watching the world go by, I do love people watching, especially people who are being dragged out by their dogs. But back to the children, suddenly from the end of the church drive lots and lots (well more than I've got claws to count them on and that's both front and back paws) of children appeared. All wearing the same coloured fur – blue tops and grey bottoms. With them were a few humans and my human guardian went up to greet them, ignoring me completely.

So as she led them all into the church, and they seemed so excited, I just had to follow, but at a safe distance. You see, children are unpredictable, I can generally see straight away if a grown-up human likes me – they smile, they bend down, they fuss me. But children are different, I've had little babies pull my tail, and toddlers grab my whiskers, so I'm not taking any chances.

There I was sat at the back of church, watching my guardian, as the children were doing so too, as she opened and closed her mouth (I do believe this is a way of communicating to each other, I'm trying to learn to lip read but it's rather hard). Then they started to wander around the church with clip boards and pencils, making notes and ticking their work sheets. A couple came near me, so I hid under the pew, but rather than walk past the little girl got down on her hands and knees and crawled under the dusty wooden pew to join me. Then, she pulled out of her hair, letting it all fall down, a lovely piece of blue ribbon, the next thing I knew she was dragging it along the floor forward and backwards, backwards and then forwards, while gently smiling at me. I couldn't resist this temptation anymore and found myself pouncing on the ribbon and running backwards and forwards after it, then catching it in my two front paws and winning the game. I could see how happy she was, as indeed so was I too.

The next thing I knew was one of the adults coming along and peering under the pew, they didn't look happy, and suddenly the smile on the child's face had disappeared, and then she disappeared from my view as she had to get up and join the others. Why weren't they happy that we were happy? What else did they want her to do in church? We had had such fun together, I liked her, and playing with her was such fun. I do hope she has a cat to fuss at her home. So after all the children had disappeared back down the church pathway I came out from under the musky pew and strutted to my guardian, she looked pleased to see me, I think she understood that sometimes you can have a special bond with someone, it may not last long, but it does matter and to remember the love and affection all your life, I'll certainly remember that young human.

Week 39 - Feathers & Feathery Things

Why do my guardians bother to bring back feathery cat toys, I hope they don't waste too much time and effort hunting for these things, because the best feathery toys are not the ones that smell bland, dyed bright colours and have bits of tinsel sparkling in the middles as they are glued to the end of a bendy stick. In my opinion, so it must be right, the best feathery toys are actual feathers from real life birds that they've lost when preening and my guardians pick up when they are walking out and about. Then tie a couple of these real smelly feathers together with an old shoe lace and you've got the best toy possible. Not only does the whiff of the bird (I prefer goose myself) fill the air as my guardian swings it around the room, but also when I catch it – which of course I do, although sometimes it takes a while and I'm out of breath from chasing it and doing back flips in the air as I turn direction to catch it, but then the taste of the old shoe lace is lovely, with essences of mud, of grass and of human sweat ingrained into the very fabric and strands of the lace. What fun! Beasley the ginger kitten likes to join in chasing the lace, but he gets too excited and gets in my way, honestly he just rushes around, no skill or strategy in his hunting – yet.

Sometimes when I'm playing chase with the pigeons I get to gently bite them and end up with a mouth full of fresh feathers. They are so light, so tickly and such good fun to bite into. Then if a few feathers have been caught in the breeze, it's great fun to chase the feathers across the lawn. The hens don't understand that I just want to taste their feathers when I chase them, honestly, what else would I be thinking? I have managed to play with some of their feathers that they have discarded after preening, which are okay but certainly not as soft or silky as goose feathers.

I would love to meet a real goose, I've seen them on the 'Moving Picture Box', so I know they are a bit smaller than me, I'd soon develop a hunting strategy to get a mouthful of their fresh feathers!

Week 40 - Hissing and Spitting

Missy isn't a nice cat. I don't hate her but I don't like her and she doesn't like me. Consequently, each time she walks past me I see her whiskers pull back, her teeth are bared and her lips snarl up and she hisses at me and then spits at me too, all this happens in less than a second as she continues to walk past me. Well for us cats, being hissed at is a really big insult. You shouldn't do it to strange cats let alone your fur family members. And it does upset me. She's a little bigger than me and a lot fluffier than me but this week I decided not to put up with her bad manners any more. So as she walked past me and started to sneer I swiped out my left paw and hit her square in the face. She looked shocked and ran off. Great I thought, that should stop her. But it didn't, later that same day she came slinking out of the doors and walked right up to me, so quick as a flash, once again I hit her in her chops, before she had time to even snarl, let alone hiss or spit. Stunned for a second, then she backed off.

Then can you believe what happened next? She re-appeared with her son Nipper who is twice the size of her and three times the size of me. Nipper is a big cat, and used to be an excellent hunter when we lived in the countryside at our last Vicarage. Nipper would catch all manner of birds and mice and even a baby bunny. So I was worried when Missy started to walk directly towards me with her big boy at her side. Two onto one is not fair. Especially when the second one is so big and I'm just a small little cat, with special needs.

I could have felt sorry for myself and ran off but then they would always know how scared I was of them. So instead I waited until they came close, and then I hit Missy with my left paw and when Nipper turned to look at his mother, I slapped him in the chops with my right paw and then ran back to the house and stood by my guardian who was busy cleaning our food bowls.

I'm learning that sometimes we shouldn't let others bully us, it's not easy and it's okay to ask for help. Hopefully Missy and Nipper will now understand they must never pick on those who are smaller than them, or those who are differently abled and gifted, because whatever I can't do (like hear) there is a lot more I can do!

Week 41 - Water and Taps

Cats aren't supposed to like water – well that's what our humans think, but we actually do like water, just in a different way to our guardians. Now they seem not to like it outdoors and will go to great lengths not to get wet in the rain, they put on extra layers of clothes, they put things on their heads and then carry above them dangerous poky sticks that unfold and stretches out above their heads, but then they bump into things as they can't see where they are going. Why do they bother with all this, as the extra layers they put on get covered in rain and have to be hung up to dry and drip all over the hall. Some of us cats enjoy the rain, we don't mind getting wet and then when we come inside we shake it off our fur and then lick the rest of it that's left – getting a free drink of fresh rain in the process. Some cats hate rain, and they stay indoors, like George, he hates the rain, but rain is lovely, watching the rain land in puddles and send ripples out across the surface – it's beautiful, and when a leaf is bending over under the weight of the droplets and then ping – it's back upright after shedding its load - it's nature's art show.

Then there is indoor water which seems to please my guardians more. Every day he has indoor rain in the bathroom. During this ritual he doesn't wear his outdoor clothes or even his indoor clothes – in fact it's no clothes at all. How odd. She likes indoor puddles and can regularly be found sitting in one. Often with foamy bubbles all around her. How very strange humans are!

But the strangeness carries on. They have special places in the house which they touch and water comes gushing out. Often with a bowl underneath it to catch the water in – but do they lick and gulp the water down, no, rather they put their food bowls and plates in this small foamy puddle and wash all the bits off. Surely they've seen me licking my cat bowl clean – that's how you clean your food bowls but hey ho, even though they are happy when I've licked cleaned my bowl for them they still insist on putting it in the foamy puddle and washing it again.

I like these special watery places and the shiny metal sticks on them, because sometimes drops of water drip from them. You can't always predict exactly when the drip is going to drop and my game is that I try and catch it as it falls to the bowl. Sometimes with my mouth and sometimes with my paw – it's such fun and my guardians, when seeing me playing my game, will often join in the fun making the drops come quicker or slower – it's such fun and I'm pleased my humans can join in the fun too.

Week 42 - Eating & Meals

Humans have strange eating habits. Cats are simple. Humans put food in a bowl for us, if we like it we eat it, if we don't like it we walk away, leaving it and giving a tail flick to show our disgust and the human learns never to try to give us bargain cat food again.

But there seems to be so much more fuss around my guardians eating. Generally it involves the 'preparation', this includes peeling of vegetables (Why? Surely the skins are the best bit as they may still have an earth tang to them) then the boiling of vegetables in a pan on the top of the oven (where incidentally I'm never allowed to walk – again why?), this varies from a few minutes, to a long time in which all the water has boiled away, and they start to smell burnt, and a guardian rushes in very stressed and tripping up over me as I dance between their legs. They must like vegetables as this makes them very grumpy.

When they have hunted and gathered all the food they want to eat, generally they take it into the front room and watch the 'Moving Picture Box' while they eat it. Generally, I leave them alone, rarely is there anything that they eat that I'd choose to lower myself to eating, certainly not their vegetables or plate of green leaves. But Fry-day is different, when he comes in with a parcel wrapped in white paper, a rich aroma of battered fish fills the house. Now I am most definitely interested in what he is eating. She just nibbles at some of the limp potato strips, when he's not looking. But I follow him into the front room and try to help him eat this yummy treat. First, I sit by his feet, in case he drops any. He doesn't. So then I sit next to him on the sofa, so he can pass me scraps. He doesn't. Then I climb onto the back of the sofa, sit by his head and reach my paw out to his fork as he shovels it into his mouth. He doesn't like this. After this I then sit right behind his head and decide to wash his hair, by licking his scalp. This makes him stop eating and generally results in him passing a handful of white fish flakes to me, which I scoff out of the palm of his hand. It's taken years to get him this trained, but it's definitely been worth all my hard work, when I have a tummy full of warm fresh fish.

Week 43 - Getting Lost & Getting Found

Oh dear, I don't know where to start. It was so horrible. So I guess I'll start at the beginning... it was Moan-day morning and as usual the Vicar, my guardian, had taken some warm sausage rolls to the volunteers who keep the churchyard looking so nice (and give me lots of fuss too). Well they smelt lovely (the sausage rolls, not the gardeners – they smelt like petrol and cut grass) so I sneaked in behind her, hoping to cheekily eat the pastry crumbs that were left, she didn't notice me and left. But I was now shut in the little porta cabin next to the church. So I enjoyed the bits of pastry but soon got bored and thought I'd explore the room, deciding to run over to the window, so I jumped up on to the top of the filing cabinet and then it happened, whoops. Because I was so fast, I lost my footing and slipped. Down and down I fell, landing on my paws, but trapped between the filing cabinet and the wall, unable to turn round, or to jump up or even back out because of the corner. I couldn't move. I couldn't even sit down, just trapped between the wall and the cabinet. It was horrible; it seemed to go on and on. The morning turned to afternoon and the afternoon turned to evening, I thought by now my guardian and her husband would miss me, without me dancing between their legs how would they know when it was tea time? Why hadn't they missed me? Obviously no one cared about me. My body ached from the pressure on it. But I couldn't move so I could relieve the aches. As evening turned to night I missed the big sofa that I can stretch out on and can roll over on while sleeping and getting my tummy tickled. The cabin was cold. I was thirsty and hungry. "Help me please," I meowed but no help came.

It was in my desperation I started to pray, my guardian does it a lot, I've watched her, well I couldn't put my paws together, I couldn't move a muscle so I just talked to God, 'Loving God please help me, my body aches, I'm hungry, thirsty and trapped. I know I don't pray as much as I should but please help me and I will try to be better, not just praying to you, but nicer to the other cats, I'll stop bullying little old Kitty on the Close, I'll be friendlier to handsome black Archie and stripy Tyger-Angel. I'll even stop hitting the pretty tabby Pips. Please help me,' and then I fell asleep – which is hard when you are standing up.

I could feel the cold metal wall of the porta cabin through my dense fur, reaching through my skin and making my bones ache more than I thought was possible. Then on my other side I could feel the cold of the metal filing cabinet pressing into me, again chilling me to the bone. Never could dawn be more welcomed than when I saw the sun rise that morning. Although the coldness went the aching stayed, who would have guessed not moving a muscle would have been so tiring. Then I felt fresh air, I'd felt it three times the day before but now I could feel the floor moving with the footsteps of the gardeners coming in for their coffee break, but they couldn't see me. So I took a deep breath and meowed – I don't know if it was loud as being deaf I can't tell but I gave it all my strength, then I smelt Pippin, she was nearby, actually very near but oddly moving from in front of the cabinet to on top of it and then back again, she kept repeating it, it was like she was dancing and mocking me. Then it was like a miracle the gardeners saw me, trapped, and they moved the cabinet so I could escape, although leaving a lot of fur behind in the tiny gap. Oh I do love them, they picked me up and looked me over, gave me a saucer of milk. I was just so happy to be free; I shall never take my freedom for granted again. Then my guardian came running in and scooped me up into her arms, holding me tighter than normal, which despite my aching bones was so lovely, it felt safe and warm, and smelt like home. I was so happy. She did the same to Pippin, I'm not sure why, I was the one that was trapped, all Pippin had done was a dance in front of the filing cabinet, teasing me.

After eating breakfast, I went to my guardian in her office and decided to join her, sitting on her cat-top. On the screen I saw the Facebook page for the church and read the messages – people had been looking for me! Lots of people, looking in their sheds and garages, some had even come to the Vicarage. Wow, posters had been put up and leaflets given to neighbours. I couldn't believe it, I thought no-one cared, but it was obvious how kind people were, all the local cats – well their guardians had been helping my guardian and also strangers I've never met – how kind, 'thank you' so much to everyone who helped. It turns out that my beloved guardian had been in the porta cabin looking for me – several times, but because I couldn't hear her I didn't meow. And Pippin, the gardeners are calling her a 'hero', apparently it was Pippin who got them to look at where I was stuck, rather than dancing and mocking me, she was getting their attention to find me. Oh what an eventful 24 hours of my life, looking back from the comfort of being stretched out on my settee, I realise how lucky I am and how loved I am and who would have guessed that God would answer my prayers through Pippin, I promise I'll not bully her anymore.

Week 44 - Birthdays and Getting Older

I'm not sure why, it's not Christmas or even Easter, but for some strange reason cards have started to appear on the mantelpiece, with pictures and words, saying 'Happy Birthday'. What is a birthday? I've been told it's a date on a calendar that shows you how old you are getting, but I don't know my birth date but I think I'm getting older. I know this because, unlike Beasley - the new little ginger kitten that has joined my home - I can't run as fast as I could, and climbing trees makes my legs hurt, and falling out of them makes all of me hurt far more than it used to. That kitten is such a pain, he doesn't wait nicely for his food, he pushes straight past me and then wolfs his food down without chewing it – I doubt if he even takes time to recognise the flavour. And he always wants to play, I'm minding my own business watching the pigeons, and he jumps on me, well I just hiss at him, I don't want any of his playful spirit around me when I'm in hunting mode, and you know what else – he just runs at the pigeons and they all fly off, I'm never going to get to wrestle a pigeon again with him annoying me all the time, he just doesn't know what good manners are or what 'cat etiquette' is either. He doesn't appreciate proper cat toys – a piece of string, in my opinion, is still the best cat toy by miles, the more chewed and dirtier it is, the better. But that's not good enough for the ginger kitten, oh no, his favourite toy was a present from his sister – Kitkat – who lives next door, she gave him a fluffy sparkly orange ball, which he loves chasing around the hall, knocking into me when he's not looking where he's going.

Back to birthdays, gosh I do seem to get distracted and wander off the point a lot these days. I know the day they came to the rescue centre I was living at and brought me home – that's my brought day. If I don't have a birthday do I stay the same age? What is it that makes me older, I wonder? Anyhow, understanding whatever it is that defines us as getting older will have to wait, as she's just put up lots more cards on the mantelpiece and I feel the urge to strut my stuff and knock them all down, which she obviously enjoys as she replaces them there again a few minutes later, so I can do it again and again – such fun!

Week 45 - Remembrance Rituals

November is a strange month for most humans. I do enjoy observing their behaviour and I've noticed November has a different feel to other months, it's a feeling rather unique to November. There is a special service in the first week of November, it's not on a Sunday but in the middle of the week, and some of the children from the Primary Schools come, not all the children but about a dozen, and there are some men in uniforms, with lots of colourful gold braid on their jackets and they bring a flag too. I love flags, chasing them as they wave through the air, but this flag is not a joyful fluttering flag but rather a sombre stiff flag. Then they carry the flag into the church and leave it on the Altar, while they have a short service. Next they all go outside again and walk around the churchyard. Interestingly, the children, in pairs then put little wooden crosses, with red poppies on them, into the soil in front of some graves, not every grave, just a few. I've noticed it's the same few graves every year. I can't help but wonder why? What's so special about these graves? I don't think they were rich or famous, as the head stones are rather simple and plain, but also elegant too.

Now there is another special service in November, this one is on a Sunday morning. Again some of the people who come wear very smart uniforms and there are more of the sombre flags. It seems very important to people to remember the names on the War Memorial in church. Everyone stands, although I'm deaf, I know they are all silent for two minutes as no-one's lips move, not at all, until the musician puts the bugle to her lips and then when she stops they talk again. What did these people give or do many, many years ago, that today is still so important that they are remembered with such strong emotions, I often see a tear in my guardian's eye as she reads the names out. What happened to these people? I'm still not sure, but like others grateful they did what they did, because we have the freedom to remember them, every year without fail, we will remember them.

Week 46 - Fires and Central Heating

Winter is cold. It's cold on my paws, it's cold on my nose, it's cold outside. But inside can be so much different – when they put the fire on in the front room it chases away the coldness of winter outside and turns inside into such a lovely warm, snuggly place to have all my catnaps. Sitting in the front room in front of the fire is prime position in the Vicarage. Missy and her son Nipper tend to hog this literal hot spot. They stretch out and bask like the whales I've seen basking on the nature programmes on the 'Moving Picture Box'. Consequently no room is left for me to nuzzle in. At the last Vicarage the fire was a real one, where he would but coal and wood on it. Watching the flames flicker in the heat of the roaring fire often sent me into a most relaxed state, where I could slip away into dreamy sleep. The smell of fires across the village would fill the evening air and be a signal for all cats to return to their homes and take their rightful place on the hearth rug. However, it was not total bliss, as every now and then the raging fire would hiss and spit out cinders, waking up the snoozing Missy and scaring nervous Nipper.

Rather than being in the cold, I've now discovered more hot spots around the Vicarage, coincidentally all these hot spots are next to the white metal things on the walls, there seems to be at least one in each room. Some get hotter than others. I've trained my guardians to put cardboard boxes that I've inspected next to these white panels, so not only do I get the warmth from them, but my lovely cardboard boxes shield me from cold drafts or breezes.

Sometimes it's easy to be jealous of others, yes Missy and lazy Nipper should share the hot spot in front of the fire, or take turns so we can all enjoy it, but rather than get bitter about Missy and fat Nipper, I've now got a much better and snug little hideout to keep warm over the cold winter months, and also another positive is I get to play an unexpected game of 'Happy Snappy' should either of them walk past. Life isn't always fair or equal, but you can always make your own fun.

Week 47 - Shoes & Slippers

Sometimes my human guardians baffle me. One of these areas of bafflement has to be their pre-occupation with what they put on their paws. Us cats have got the right idea – come rain or shine we go out as we are, sometimes my paws get wet, sometimes they get frozen, and sometimes they feel the softness of fresh spring grass under my paws. It's wonderful – the tingling of my paws on crisp snow that crunches as it compacts under my weight as I walk along. The sensation of walking on water (well not actually but nearly) as I slide on ice. The warmth of striding out on a carpet and of course the luxury around my toes as I pad my way through a deep piled rug – oh what bliss.

So what do my human guardians do? Well they seem to miss out on all these fantastic and diverse sensations by putting not just one layer of stuff on their hind paws but two. First goes their indoor footwear – which is generally a knitted thing that they pull over their feet – and it hides their wiggle toes (which I do enjoy playing with when they stick them out of the duvet when in bed) but then before they go outside they add another layer – I think they call these 'shoes' because they shoe away every sensation from their feet. These shoes are dangerous – occasionally they have stood on my paw in these shoes and they hurt. I try to avoid them but Beasley the kitten he loves shoes, not just playing with the ones that have laces, but he enjoyed sitting inside them – probably pretending he is in a boat as my male guardian has huge shoes. He leaves his muddy boots by the back door and we all love to have a sniff around them and guess where the mud has come from. Sometimes hers are pretty colours, sometimes they are raised at the back, and have straps – that are good to chew, especially when made from animal skin.

And there is another fascinating thing about shoes – the smell! Because my guardians wear a pair most days, the sweat from their feet builds up and up and sometimes boy do their shoes pong – there's no polite way to put it, if only they would learn from us cats, my paws never ever smell!

Week 48 - Purring

Cats have many amazing qualities. Purring is unique to us cats. It's something that just happens when we are happy, I can't make it happen and I can't stop it from happening. Purring is such a special feeling it's hard to explain. My human guardians do make me purr, on a cold winter's evening when the fire is on and I'm on the sofa, to stretch my feet out to touch her as she's sharing my sofa, then to feel her gently stroke my tummy, then my head and then to delicately scratch under my chin - well it's just pure bliss, or should that be 'purr-bliss'. I've noticed when I'm purring away my guardians also seem happier, they can't purr so I purr more for them too.

Sometimes I can feel the vibrations of the purrs from the other cats. Jasper has a deep purr that makes the sofa vibrate from one end to the other. Even when touching paws I can hardly tell if Pips is purring as her purr is so gentle. Then there is Nipper who when he purrs the vibrations can be felt everywhere, it's like he starts up a motor and everything shudders while he is ticking over. Every cat has a different purr, we are all rather unique.

Recently she was poorly and spent all day sleeping on the sofa - she had come in rather late the night before, smelling differently and laughing far more than she normally does when she comes home. I'm not sure where she had been, but he wasn't best pleased to see her in that state. So I lay next to her and purred away for hours, I think she knew I was trying to heal her. My mum explained to me how a cat's purr vibrates and resonates at such a frequency that it actually helps humans heal, especially if they have any broken bones. Well I don't know about that, but I do know my guardian was feeling a lot better by the time it was my supper time and I got a tuna treat for being so caring.

Week 49 - Knitting and Wool

Sometimes guests come and stay with my guardians at the Vicarage. I really enjoy us having visitors, not just because I get extra fuss and attention but often I get sneaky treats from them too. Her mother is one of my favourites, not that she really gives me much fuss but because she brings with her balls of wool. A ball of wool is the traditional toy for us cats and still a favourite with me. The game starts when she is sat down on the sofa, gets out of her lavender fragranced bag her long thin sticks and then starts to wrap the end of a ball of wool around their pointy ends and then a rhythm starts as she carries on wrapping the wool around the ends, with a strip of the knitted fabric slowly forming under them.

When she is engrossed in her sticks I take the chance to play with the wool. She leaves the ball unguarded, so I nip in and gently pat it away from her, it rolls a little, so I pat it a little more. This action goes unnoticed by her, so I get a little more daring, kicking the ball a little harder and further away – under the coffee table, through the wide legs and then a sideways kick between the narrow legs. If I was a footballer it would have been a beautiful goal.

Then she looks up from her sticks and straight at me with confusion, and then noticing that the thread of wool is now tight, she tries to pull it, it doesn't give. Now the little ball is firmly tied in a messy chaos of thread under the coffee table and around the chair. She looks angrily at me, and one of my guardians comes running in the room. Whoops, I'm in trouble now. His face is more interesting, he's trying to hide his feelings, is he angry, no, he turns away and I can see him suppressing a laugh and a smile spreads across his face. He waves to me and I run to him, I know that wave, I recognise when they give me a wave if I go to them then I get a fuss. And sure enough this time is no exception. He picks me up in his big strong arms, but gently and smiling he takes me off to the kitchen, where he opens a little tin of my favourite cat food, that's normally only a supper time treat. I think he really appreciates my wool-ball skills!

Week 50 - Computers & Cat-Tops

My human guardians have some strange past-times. None more so than when they sit and stare at a screen, I can understand why they might stare at the 'Moving Picture Box' often as it has nature programmes on it and they, like me, can practise their hunting skills. Although I don't actually

see them hunting much, and when I do see them out in the garden it seems to be more about trimming the lawn and clearing out plants from the edges of the garden. Which is such a shame as I love long grass, it's great fun to hide in and then to play the 'Happy Snappy' game with passing cats.

But it's this small screen thingy that confuses me. They sit for ages staring at it – just like when I'm staring out from under a bush waiting for a pigeon to land so I can chase it. But for them no pigeons ever land but still they keep staring at the letters, figures and occasional pictures they have on these screens. Sometimes they have moving pictures on these little screens but they never practise their pouncing, like I do with the big 'Moving Picture Box'. Let's face it, I've shown them how to do it enough times, that now they generally move me when I'm giving them another lesson as the 'Moving Picture Box' shows a programme about squirrels or other suitable nature shows.

They do seem to be concentrating, and often tap at the little keys in front of the screen, so being helpful I try to help and will go and take the opportunity to join them by sitting on the keys for them, I do pride myself on how helpful I am and refer to this household gizmo as a 'cat-top' as a cat should always be sitting on top of it. Well this never seems to be greeted with the positive, happy response I expect and deserve, rather I often get picked up in a grumpy huff and put onto the nearby floor. Being the helpful cat, I again try to help them, but this time will lie across the keypad, covering as many of those pesky keys as I can, but again I get picked up and dumped elsewhere. My final offer of help involves me sitting by their side and then lying across their wrists, so they can still touch the keys but in a rather more limited way. I think they appreciate this as often it results in them getting up, leaving their 'cat-top' and getting a nice snack for me. When this happens, I know I can leave them to carry on with their screen staring a while, so after my snack I go and have a little catnap elsewhere, leaving them in peace – a peace which I don't think they really understand.

Week 51 - It's Christmas Time

So here it is 'Merry Christmas' everyone. I love December for so many reasons, firstly my human guardians are happier, yes they rush around a bit more but it's with smiles and laughter, even when I wind myself between their ankles and trip them up. Then things change in my home, I'm not normally keen on change but I like these changes – pretty colourful cards start appearing on the mantelpiece – they are so much fun to knock over. They hang tinsel around the mirrors and pictures, as it dangles, it twinkles in the light and I just can't resist pulling on it to see how far I can drag it down, sometimes the picture comes down too, whoops.

Then of course my favourite – the Christmas tree, I'm not sure why they bring a real tree into the house and decorate it, unless of course it is for me to play with, so that's what I do. Every night I see how many of the shiny baubles I can knock off. She must love this game, because every morning she picks them up and puts them back on the tree, but a little higher and secured a little tighter, it is more of a challenge, but I still manage to knock them off again and so this game continues.

Things change a little at church too, I'm getting more regular at going to the services and have been known to curl up and fall asleep for the entire service. But in December it's brilliant, the church gets packed with happy people and excited children – especially at the service when they hold an orange with a big candle in it and 12 sweets stuck in the top. There is even a service in the middle of the night, everyone is very joyful at that midnight service, like something special has happened. However the one thing I don't like, is that before she goes to do the midnight service, she has a tradition of dressing us cats up in silly clothes, that sparkle and have bells on. I don't feel very dignified at all, but it keeps her happy, humans are simple creatures after all.

All this seasonal fun is very tiring for a little cat, so I love it when in the evening the fire is burning, and the room is 'toasty' warm, I can curl up in my basket and fall asleep, dreaming of more fun games the following day, but no more silly clothes – please!

Week 52 - Happy New Year

Happy New Year! I'm not 100% sure what 'New Year' is, but I'm pleased it's happy. I wasn't very happy recently, yes of course I love Christmas and everything was busy and fun, but something has changed. It's George. I've noticed how he and Pips spent a lot of time together in church, I like church but not as much as them, they both enjoy the attention and fuss from all the kind people but I'm still a little shy and nervous. George doesn't want to play with me like he used to. The things we used to do together, he doesn't want to do anymore. Then I see him and Pips happy together. Playing in the churchyard, like we used to do, and enjoying the bright morning sunshine sitting together on the wall, watching the dogs go by.

I could be upset, I could be jealous, and I could be heartbroken, but I'm trying to be positive and to think differently. I'm pleased George and Pips are friends, I'm pleased they have fun together, they are both lovely. By being nasty, jealous and bitter, the only one I hurt is myself. Things happen for a reason, special friends come into our lives and sometimes they can't stay, but to be thankful for the good times shared together.

I'm now spending more time in the garden playing 'chase' with the squirrels and 'tag' with the pigeons, but I'm not always on my own, Darwin, George's younger brother now comes most mornings to sit beside me under the tree and watch the squirrels run along the branches. He's great, we even play 'chase' with each other up the trees. We have lots of fun together, especially when he chases the Vicar's hens, they flap their wings and get into such a panic, silly hens, he won't hurt them. Life doesn't stay still, things happen, and who knows what this next year will bring, but I really do hope it's a happy one.

The Final Entry

Well I've done it, every week for the past year I've made a little log of my activities, thoughts, reflections and observations. I'm not sure why, but does one need to be sure of something to do it? Do you need to know the exact destination before setting out? Or can you focus on enjoying the journey? Life is a journey, every cat's life journey is unique to them, just as their guardians are unique and bizarre to them too.

I've had great fun observing and trying to understand my human guardians over this past year, I think now I have more questions than answers, and perhaps that is the way it will always be. But I do feel closer to them, closer to understanding what's important to them and understanding the truth about love. Love isn't envious, and I've tried not to be envious of the other cats, and the time my guardians spend with them. Love isn't resentful, and I don't resent being abandoned as a kitten, otherwise I might not have been found by these guardians. Love isn't arrogant – okay I struggle with this one, but when you are being judged for something you can't do, for a disability, rather than for your many, many abilities you need to take pride in every achievement you make, especially winning at 'Hide and Seek'. Love does not rejoice in wrong doings, so I've tried to behave, really I have, even when playing the 'Happy Snappy' game.

I know it's the love of my guardians that bears all the mischievous things I do, because of their love for me – they believe in me, which is probably why they entered me into the various Pet Competitions, and love hopes all things – I guess they hoped I'd win those stupid competitions. Because of the abundance of their love they endured all the things I got up to; locked in the porta cabin over night; shut up in church all evening; trapped in the garage and so the list goes on. But this I do know, true love, the love of my guardians for me, and me for them, well that love never ends.

So if you can, please give a home to a rescue cat ... your home and your heart will be filled with more love than you ever imagined possible.